Summary Bun Biography | R Publishing: Includes Summary of Grain Brain & Summary of Grant

ABBEY BEATHAN

Legal & Disclaimer

The information contained in this book is not designed to replace or take the place of any form of medicine or professional medical advice. The information in this book has been provided for educational and entertainment purposes only.

The information contained in this book has been compiled from sources deemed reliable, and it is accurate to the best of the Author's knowledge; however, the Author cannot guarantee its accuracy and validity and cannot be held liable for any errors or omissions. Changes are periodically made to this book. You must consult your doctor or get professional medical advice before using any of the suggested remedies, techniques, or information in this book. Images used in this book are not the same as of that of the actual book. This is a totally separate and different entity from that of the original book titled: "Grain Brain"

Upon using the information contained in this book, you agree to hold harmless the Author from and against any damages, costs, and expenses, including any legal fees potentially resulting from the application of any of the information provided by this guide. This disclaimer applies to any damages or injury caused by the use and application, whether directly or indirectly, of any advice or information presented, whether for breach of contract, tort, negligence, personal injury, criminal intent, or under any other cause of action.

You agree to accept all risks of using the information presented inside this book. You need to consult a professional medical practitioner in order to ensure you are both able and healthy enough to participate in this program.

Table of Contents

The Book at a Glance

Despite the many technological breakthroughs, we are suffering from slow-acting diseases which affect the brain. There's also the problem with the prevalence of obesity. So, what if I tell you that a major factor that triggers these conditions is the food you eat?

This is what *Grain Brain* is going to show you.

Myths will be debunked, and you will gain knowledge about the processes that occur in your body and brain. Know what happens because of what you eat and where damages are inflicted.

Discover how carb and sugar-filled diets trigger hormonal changes, which affect your overall wellbeing. What you considered your staple is actually what's ruining your health from the inside out. One of the most dreaded illnesses is Alzheimer's. It's a brain disease that stems from inflammation like many other ailments.

Unbeknownst to many, food filled with gluten and carbohydrates trigger inflammation which is the major cause of brain degradation and various other related cases such as anxiety, depression, and even the simple headaches you get every now and then. Additional accounts from David

Perlmutter's patients further prove that by properly identifying gluten sensitivity in those with disorders, improvements can be achieved.

Interestingly, cholesterol and fats are in fact not bad for you at all. Fats are a vital energy source and cholesterol promotes more active and faster neurological connections. Carbohydrates and sugars, on the other hand, promote obesity and diabetes. A sudden boost of sugar levels in the body increases the rate by which insulin is produced. If the insulin level becomes too high, the body becomes resistant to the hormone and fails to properly regulate blood sugar levels. Also, the body starts storing more fat in the cells whenever there's a spike in one's blood sugar levels.

Fortunately, there is still hope for people with diseases and disorders. And if you are one, remember that with a proper diet, exercise, and sleep, you would be able to control your genetic destiny and take proper care of your mental faculties. This would allow you to avoid the brain diseases that are common in today's society.

Limit your food intake to natural proteins and fats, and keep off processed sugars and carbs. Make it a point to be physically active during the day, even if it's just a simple walk or cleaning the house. See to it that you get at least

7

seven to eight hours of good night's sleep. Note that supplements are also good for you, especially those for replenishing vitamins and minerals.

With all these, you would be able to improve your brain health in no time—and you'll manage to protect yourself from some of the most feared diseases, as early as possible.

With *Grain Brain*, you can start living a healthier life by learning how to choose what's best for you to eat. Keep your brain heathy and start building better connections for a faster and clearer memory.

Introduction

Against the Grain

Before modernization completely took over, people usually die from old age or from the early symptoms of diseases like pneumonia, tuberculosis, and the like. Today the causes of death boil down to specific ailments, unique from person to person, like heart attack, dementia, diabetes, and cancer.

The human body can be compared to a house. As both grows old, their structural state start to decline and would soon be needing repairs and patches. However, repairs merely relieve temporary problems. There can be no complete recovery without a total overhaul. The human body as a structure, just like a house, has its limits.

Alzheimer's disease, a brain disorder and a type of dementia, is among the biggest problems you could face. Studies have proven that people fear dementia more than cancer or even death. The fear of losing one's memory and reasoning affects not only the old, but also younger people.

There are a lot of ideas surrounding Alzheimer's and the most common is the belief that the disease runs in the genes and becomes unavoidable as you age. However, David Perlmutter begs to differ. According to him, brain disorders are neither embedded in your genes nor unavoidable. Instead, the culprits are the believed-to-be healthy modern grains considered as our society's everyday food staple.

With support from scientific studies and modern physiological perspectives, David aims to prove his claim through *Grain Brain* and provide a new approach towards understanding and battling brain disorders.

Compared to methods for battling chronic diseases like cancer, diabetes, and other lifestyle-induced disorders, those directed to caring for our brain's health is evidently fewer and uncommon. Most treat brain disorders as a normal part of aging and not based on one's lifestyle. Again, David says that it's not the case. According to him, brain-related problems are related to the shift in our diet over the previous century which continues to contribute to our cognitive decline.

He mentions that recent medical literature has long recognized the negative relation between the two, only that it has not been made public yet. This conflict raised questions in both of scientists and doctors' minds about the ideas on health and nutrition.

As a neurologist and a member of the American College of Nutrition, he started this unique perspective on the correlation between the brain and food we eat. Fully

10

equipped with the understanding of this new science, he wants to act and push forward with his newfound belief through *Grain Brain*.

Grain Brain will be demonstrating how modern diet continues to challenge our physiology with modern hybrids and genetically modified food without genetically preparing the body first. The book will also be highlighting the connection between several brain disorders (like the fact that diabetes increases the chances to develop Alzheimer's) and how diseases that seem unlikely to affect the brain are related to mental dysfunctions in ways we have never imagined.

With his 35 years of experience with brain diseases, David, through *Grain Brain*, aims to present lifestyle changes that promote brain-health awareness instead of relying on illness-centered treatments to reduce the risk for brain disease in the future.

He guarantees that with *Grain Brain*, you will be looking at life from a whole new perspective. If you fear that it may be too late, David says that you should not panic and instead take control of your life from now then on. The book has been divided into three parts with comprehensive questionnaires in between to help readers assess how their daily habits affect their brain's long-term health.

Self-Assessment

What Are Your Risk Factors?

Unbeknownst to many, brain diseases are also influenced by our nutrition and lifestyle choice. It does not befall us by chance.

Before going into the science behind the claim on the relation of brain disorders and nutrition, we will be starting with a questionnaire to reveal some of your habits that are negatively affecting you right now.

Testing, Testing, 1-2-3

Risk factors can now be accurately profiled per individual through various laboratory tests. Knowing the tests will help you better grasp *Gran Brain*'s concepts. Below are the tests mentioned throughout the book:

- Fasting Blood Glucose: measures the amount of glucose in your blood after eight hours of fasting. This is a common test to check if you have diabetes.

- Hemoglobin A1C: this is one of the best tests to predict brain atrophy (damage of proteins in brain due to blood sugar). It reveals the average blood sugar for a 90-day period.

- Fructosamine: similar to A1C but only provides results over the past two to three weeks.

- Fasting Insulin: an effective early warning system for diabetes.

- Homocysteine: a test for identifying high levels of amino acid.

- C-reactive Protein (CRP): for identifying signs of inflammation.

- Cyrex Array 3 and 4: tests for gluten sensitivity.

Part 1

The Whole Grain Truth

This part is dedicated to finding out how most carbs are composed of ingredients that can incur damage to the nervous system and lead to the development of disorders like dementia and depression.

Chapter 1

The Cornerstone of Brain Disease

What You Don't Know About Inflammation

Compared to their ancestors, modern humans live a life of safety, security, and luxury. This is especially true in when it comes to food and healthcare.

In the older times, death came in swifter. The increase in the average life expectancy is only because of improvements on infant mortality and childcare. Unfortunately, solutions for many illnesses that affect the older age groups are still out of reach. In modern medicine, doctors are taught to tackle illnesses by considering one of its major causes: inflammation. However, doctors have also encountered diseases that no prescribed drug or therapy can cure, like Alzheimer's and cancer.

Before proceeding to the discussion of the connection between the brain and inflammation, consider that a brain disease such as Alzheimer's, the most feared form of dementia, is a type of diabetes triggered by diet alone.

Your cognitive health and eating habits might not be unrelated after all.

Alzheimer's Disease—Type 3 Diabetes?

Our bodies are similar in physiological function to those of our ancestors. Both need fat and carb to perform various bodily processes. However, there is one clear difference. Our ancestors had to go through more trouble to access food. They get nutrients from natural sources (like wild animals and plants). On the other hand, the modern times offer us convenient options, often in the form of processed products.

This difference in dietary habits has everything to do with the neurological diseases or disorders we are currently experiencing.

To provide better understanding, David outlines the relationship between the brain and diabetes. According to him, Alzheimer's and diabetes are common not in the symptoms they show, but in the food we take that triggers them.

Diabetes is a disease where a person's blood sugar content is too high due to the insufficient amount of insulin. There are two types of diabetes: type 1 and type 2.

Type 1 is caused by the body's immune response to insulin. This type of diabetes is incurable and can only supported by continuous doses of insulin. Type 2, on the other hand, can be prevented through proper lifestyle and diet. It only occurs when a person has taken too much sugar—at amounts greater than what that can be handled by the body's normal insulin production. Due to the excessive sugar intake, the body adapts to the demand and requires higher levels of insulin than its production can handle. This insufficiency in the hormone leads to spikes in blood sugar and requires the afflicted to take more insulin.

However, David says that insulin does not only absorb sugar from the body but also promotes growth, build-up of fat, and inflammation. As insulin levels increase, the body's normal physiological processes also get affected, leading to the development of other diseases.

According to studies, the lack of insulin contributes to the build-up of plaques that are commonly seen in brains of Alzheimer patients. The plaques are odd proteins that hijack the brain, replacing the normal brain cells. Therefore, patients with diabetes have double the chances of getting Alzheimer's compared to those not suffering from the condition.

The Silent Brain on Fire

As a neurologist, David had his own share of difficult times with a patient's family when he had to explain why the patient is suffering from Alzheimer's. As hard as it may be, he confronts them with the truth that the patient may be suffering from the disease because he/she has lived with high blood sugar levels even without diabetes, went on a low-fat diet that minimized cholesterol, eaten too many carbs, or has undiagnosed gluten sensitivity.

Most people doubt David when he mentions that gluten sensitivity is a major issue when it comes to neurological impairments, saying that if he is referring to celiac disease then that's simply far-off. However, 40% of the global population do not have the capacity to process gluten, even without celiac disease. When patients approach him saying they have tried everything, he would always prescribe that they eliminate gluten from their diet and the results continue to surprise him.

Doctors have indeed found one major source of disease, which is inflammation. But most still fail to realize what causes the inflammation. And their findings point to one of the major instigators: gluten—a carbohydrate and a prominent trigger of the brain's inflammatory pathways. The brain is often silent when it's affected by our diet. It shows no signs of impairment until the effects are already irreversible.

To help you avoid the path to neurological impairment, David has devised ways on how to develop control over your genetic destiny. But you must first learn the truth about cholesterol. *Grain Brain* might be taking away most of the carbs, but it will also be replacing those with food that are commonly deemed unhealthy but are actually not, such as eggs, butter, cheese, and healthy vegetables.

Once your body starts adapting to a low-carb diet and learns to rely on protein and fat, you will soon get a noticeable boost in energy. Also, you'll find it easier to lose weight. You will even achieve better sleep, enhanced memory, and improved brain health.

Inflammation Gets Cerebral

Going back to the topic of inflammation, most people don't fully understand what it really is. Aside from it being the appearance of redness after getting bitten by an insect or the soreness brought by arthritis, inflammation is the body's response to stress that defends it from potential harm such as toxins. But there is more to that process.

Inflammation is made for spot treatments. But if the body is constantly exposed to an irritant, then inflammation also becomes a constant thing. However, prolonged episodes of inflammation would lead to the production of harmful toxins, which would cause loss of cell function and consequently, destruction.

More and more people are beginning to recognize the relation of increased inflammation to coronary heart disease more than cholesterol does. However, when it comes to brain disease, people are more hesitant to believe in new perspectives even when backed with scientific findings.

According to David, this is entirely because brain inflammation cannot be felt or recognized. The brain lacks pain receptors and therefore lacks the ability to feel inflammation. To further support this claim, studies have shown that people with brain disorders have high levels of cytokines, cellular mediators of inflammation. And through new imaging technology, brains of Alzheimer's patients showed that the cells play a vital role in producing inflammatory cytokines. Inflammation is indeed related to brain degeneration.

In the core of chronic inflammation lies oxidative stress, which is essentially the biological counterpart to

20

rusting. Like inflammation, it is also a natural process but is extremely harmful if it goes out of control.

The oxidation process mainly involves single-electron oxygen molecules (which are produced because of things like stress) robbing other electrons of their molecules. Oxidation produces chain reactions which leads to inflammation. Most people who have high degrees of oxidation are diagnosed with increased levels of inflammation too.

In conclusion, reduced oxidation would also mean reduction of inflammation. Nutrients like vitamins E, C, and A help in this process by donating their free electrons to the needy single-electron oxygen molecules. However, modern industry has continued to process food in a way that strips it of the nutrients we need.

Grain Brain presents ways on how to avoid oxidation and consequently decrease inflammation too. Moreover, David mentions that managing inflammation does not only rely on our diet, but on our sleep and physical activity as well.

The Cruel Irony: Statins

Our body needs cholesterol to function properly.

Contrary to how they are advertised, cholesterol-lowering statins are doing more harm than good. David says that before proceeding, you must first believe that cholesterol is good, and it is not to blame especially in the case of coronary heart disease.

Chapter 2

The Sticky Protein

Gluten's Role in Brain Inflammation (It's Not Just About Your Belly)

To David, gluten is a modern poison. It has become a major part of the pattern in his diagnosis with his patients. By recommending that they try a gluten-free diet, patients with chronic headache, bipolar disorder symptoms, and persistent tremors have begun seeing positive results months after.

Just as if the society is in on the discovery, more and more products are made gluten-free due to the rising number of people who want to purchase them. David mentions that Yahoo's 2011 sports article on Novak Djokovic's gluten-free diet played a major role in influencing others to try it too. But why exactly is gluten considered harmful?

The Glue of Gluten

Gluten is the Latin word for "glue". As its etymology implies, it is protein that has adhesive properties and is a major ingredient of gummy and chewy products. It's of importance in baking (specifically in leavening) and is in almost every thickening product there is (such as those in soups). And like any other protein, gluten can trigger allergic reactions.

Gluten is composed of a pair of protein groups, namely glutenins and gliadins. Sensitivity to any of the two or even part of their property will trigger inflammation.

Most people mistake gluten sensitivity for celiac disease. However, what most people do not know is that celiac disease is just the result of extreme gluten sensitivity that is directed at the small intestine. In reality, gluten sensitivity can harm any organ while leaving the small intestine unharmed. As long as there's a chance that a person is gluten-sensitive, his brain and body are also at risk.

Food sensitivities occur when the body does not have the capability to digest certain ingredients and triggers immune system responses that release inflammatory chemicals, which include killer cells, to eliminate harm. However, it also damages the surrounding tissues and leads to more problems—even autoimmune diseases.

This is particularly detrimental when dealing with sensitivity from gluten's component called gliadin. This leads to the production of more antibodies. Gliadins combine with antibodies to form an antibody pair that turns on specific genes in a specific immune cell. This in turn leads to the

24

production of inflammatory cytokine chemicals that harm the brain. Once started, the process will continue and produce more cytokines of the same kind and further attack and damage the brain. This is what happens when a patient suffers from a brain disorder. There are even some cases in which minor gluten sensitivities are mistaken as impairment of the mental faculties.

Simply put, gluten sensitivity is not limited to cases involving celiac disease. It can also harm other organs in the body, especially the brain.

Celiac Through the Centuries

Even though the association between gluten sensitivity and neurological disorders are rarely mentioned in medical literature, celiac disease has been on the record since the first century A.D., as first described by Aretaeaus of Cappadocia as an 'abdominal' ailment.

It wasn't until the 17th century when they started interfering with the patients' diets. And it took a good two centuries before they started figuring out what causes it. It was Dr. Willem Dicke who discovered the connection of wheat flour and celiac back in the 1940s after the sudden drop in the disease's prevalence during the Dutch famine.

Then it took a few more decades before technology

became capable of studying and identifying the relationship between cognitive impairments and the culprit, gluten.

The Bigger Picture

Gluten sensitivity is not limited to celiac disease, which affects the gut. It is an underestimated enemy that constantly attacks the brain without indication.

A Glut of Gluten in Modern Food

With the advancements in technology, gluten has evolved farther than what it was during our ancestors' times. From the discovery of genetic modification, we have continued to breed and produce food with selective characteristics. And gluten is part of that big boom.

According to studies, consumption of food with gluten triggers the same brain receptors that opium does. Since it gives the same effect as that of an addictive drug, it's no wonder that modern food manufacturing has gluten all-over it. As more food gets more gluten, obesity becomes more rampant and various other diseases too.

Bottomline is, people have remained far too long in the darkness about the true effects of our daily gluten-filled consumption. In addition, fats are continuously avoided, and carbs are treated as a staple. However, instead of keeping us brain-healthy, that kind of diet might just be doing the reverse for our mental faculties.

Chapter 3

Attention, Carboholics and Fat Phobics

Surprising Truths About Your Brain's Real Enemies and Lovers

Contrary to common knowledge, cholesterol and fats are not bad for your health. Gluten is what we need to cut from our diet, as well as the excess carbohydrates that we find in everyday food products.

Fat Genes and Phat Science

The appearance of modern agriculture has eliminated the scarcity of food sources and the difficulty that people encounter during famine. However, the body's genes cannot be easily changed. Like our ancestors', our physiology still needs fats as means for surviving the famine that will never come. Even to this day, the "fat gene", which is responsible for producing fat stores, still exists. And modern humans eat carbohydrates almost every day, activating the fat genes daily. Thus, the continuous build-up of unnecessary fat storage and the increasing problem with obesity.

A study by Mayo Clinic also showed that older people who tend to have a daily diet of mostly carbs increased their risk for Alzheimer's by 400%. And those who

28

have mainly fats and proteins have reduced chances of suffering from cognitive impairment, especially those who consume omega-3 fats from fish regularly.

Further studies showed that cholesterol is highly related to memory functions and longevity. Unlike what common knowledge dictates, it is not cholesterol that is bad for the brain but the oxidized carrier proteins. These carrier proteins are responsible for transporting good cholesterol to the brain for improved function. So, the solution is preventing rapid oxidations and not necessarily decreasing the amount of cholesterol or the carrier proteins.

A Little History

Back in the 1900s, the human diet was centered on equal portions of saturated and unsaturated fat together with servings of meat, eggs, and butter. By the twentieth century, the lipid hypothesis took over and the previous staples in the diet were replaced by food trends that are low-fat or cholesterol-free.

Then scientists started associating fatty diets to fatty arteries and heart diseases as the mortality rate rose. As response, the government released the "Dietary Goals for United States" and food manufacturers started focusing on providing products full of carbohydrates and processed oils as replacements for the 'bad fats'.

However, following a low-fat diet did not improve the statistics for heart disease. Also, several population studies have disagreed with the low-fat notion, providing support for the belief that fats are indeed beneficial.

Back in 2010, Dr. Donald Miller from the University of Washington predicted that the trend for low-fat and high-carb diet will end once the health benefits of fats and cholesterol are made known to the public. It is only a matter of time before we finally get ourselves back on track. But come to think of it, if fats are not the culprit to the diseases, then what is?

Carbs, Diabetes, and Brain Disease

Studies show that carbohydrate consumption can lead to diabetes which, as discussed in the previous chapters, is a major factor in brain disease development. Resistance to insulin robs the body of the capability to break down proteins that build plaques in the brain. Also, high levels of blood sugar triggers biological reactions that results to damaged cells and inflammation.

Get the Facts on Fat: Your Brain's Best Friend

Carbohydrate-rich diet promotes inflammation and

fat storage as it triggers the production of insulin which halts the breakdown of naturally stored fats in the body.

Whereas dietary fats such as omega-3 and monosaturated ones reduce inflammation and play key roles in regulating the immune system. Fats are also vital in absorbing essential vitamins such as vitamins A, D, E, and K. Lack of these vitamins normally result to various congenital diseases.

Contrary to modern advice, consumption of saturated fats from natural sources such as eggs and meat is actually good for your body and its various physiological processes.

The Case for Cholesterol

No matter what kind of cholesterol, there is no good or bad ones. In fact, it a fifth of the brain is essentially cholesterol and the synapses are dependent on its presence. It plays a vital role in brain communication and serves as an antioxidant that prevents further oxidation from taking place.

The real culprits to brain deterioration are food rich in carbohydrates. Unlike the common belief that our body runs mainly on glucose, fats which are considered a 'super fuel' are completely overlooked.

Modern society continues to think negatively of the presence of fats and cholesterol in the human diet. Pharmaceutical companies take advantage of this misinformation which takes us to another problem: the statin epidemic.

The Statin Epidemic and the Link to Brain Dysfunction

Several studies have linked the intake of statins to loss of cognitive function. Since cholesterol fosters healthy neuron transmission in the brain and is the main source for the body's production of vitamin D, the lipid-lowering effect of statins may actually lead to the development brain diseases.

How Carbs—Not Cholesterol—Cause High Cholesterol

Consumption of dietary cholesterol is vital in supporting bodily functions. The low-cholesterol diet most people adhere to triggers the body's alarm system, resulting to the synthesis of cholesterol from the surplus carbohydrates we consume. This is turn leads to the production of excess amounts of cholesterol. Although having high cholesterol is not something to be feared, as it is a poor indicator of heart disease.

Sex Ed: It's All in Your Head

Believe it or not, most patients who took statins have suffered from low testosterone levels for it lowers cholesterol levels and inhibits testosterone-producing enzymes.

Chapter 4

Not A Fruitful Union

This Is Your Brain on Sugar (Natural or Not)

A number of experts believe that sugar is a toxin. It is also considered an empty calorie. The body processes a sugar depending on its characteristics. Fructose goes through your liver, while glucose gets used by the body's cells.

Sugar and Carbs 101

Carbohydrates are basically chains of sugar molecules, therefore it is logical to assume that all sugars contribute to obesity. However, carbs vary in their capabilities to raise blood sugar. The greater its capability, the faster it is digested, and the more fattening it is. In addition, consumption of easy-to-breakdown monosaccharides (glucose) triggers insulin production, which in turn signals fat storage. The more we consume sugar, the greater the risk for obesity and diabetes, which lead to other diseases such as dementia and cancer.

The Death Knell in Diabetes

The longer a patient has diabetes, the higher the risk for suffering cognitive impairments. Intake of insulin also heightens the risk by 200%. The connection between

34

Alzheimer's and constantly high blood sugar levels is described by a proposed mechanism involving the increased production of advanced glycation end products.

One Mad Cow and Many Clues to Neurological Disorders

Proteins basically shape the human body as it codes our genetic material and forms a distinctive shape unique to its function. They also act as master switches to physiological processes. The mad-cow disease that swept the globe in the 1990s was found to originate from the effect of deviant proteins that inflict damage from cell to cell. It is related to diseases (such as diabetes, dementia, and cataracts) that involve deformed proteins, which can be toxic. But for ailments that do not manifest until later, the glycation end products are to blame.

Glycation is a natural bodily process that involves the bonding of sugar molecules to proteins. However, rapid glycation causes proteins to become misshapen, thus causing the aforementioned diseases. The solution is to slow down glycation which is impossible with a high-carb diet that supplies sugar.

Glycation of LDLs, cholesterol's carrier proteins, is

also linked with the increase in oxidation and cognitive decline. One way to reduce oxidative stress is to limit glycation, which can be done by cutting down on your sugar intake.

Early Action

Aside from monitoring your fasting blood sugar, your fasting insulin level is also important since spiked insulin levels are predictors of diabetes, which as we know causes cognitive impairment. The lower the insulin levels, the better. It is a sign that blood sugar is under control and your pancreas is not overworked.

The Fatter You Are, The Smaller Your Brain

Being too fat may also incur brain damage. Accumulated fat in between our internal organs (aka visceral fat), triggers inflammatory pathways and signals molecules that disrupts the body's hormonal actions. Excess body fat not only increases the body's resistance to insulin but inflammation as well, further driving the brain towards deterioration.

The Power of Weight Loss (Besides What You Already Know)

Losing fat helps improve your insulin sensitivity and

36

reduces your risk of having diabetes. It is also best to partner it with a high-fat low-carb diet for maximized health benefits.

An Apple A Day

You may be wondering just how you can avoid getting fat while maintaining a high-fat diet. Well, David says that we can, and we should—for changing the fat genome we had for a million years won't be worth the effort.

Chapter 5

The Gift of Neurogenesis and Controlling Master Switches

How to Change Your Genetic Destiny

Contrary to common belief, brain diseases are not programmed genetically. Rather they are brought upon by our lifestyle and daily habits. Although genetics may be a factor in determining our health risks, we ultimately determine our fate. In fact, we can re-program our genes and enhance the expression of healthy ones by managing our diet.

The Story of Neurogenesis

As a neurologist, David had his own share of experiences with neuroscience. He paid particular attention to the subject of the brain's lack of regeneration ability. To him, it made no sense that every other kind of cell in the body could do so except for the brain; even the heart regenerates its cells as well. It was only until recently that scientist and doctors alike began discovering the brain's self-renewing qualities leading to a new science named neuroplasticity.

Neural stem cells exist within our brains, basically enabling us to experience stem cell therapy all throughout our lives. This discovery raised hopes in finding clues to curing brain diseases and gave rise to new treatments. The process is triggered by our DNA that produces a protein called brain-derived neurotrophic factor (BDNF), which is affected by our lifestyle.

This Is Your (New) Brain on Exercise

Aside from offering physical benefits, exercise also contributes to the activation of the brain's growth hormone.

Caloric Restriction

Population studies reveal the benefits of having low-calorie diets in relation to the risk of having brain disease. This is related to how big of a factor sugar is in our increased calorie consumption. Elevated blood sugar levels and obesity is related to reduced BDNF, while reduced appetite is associated with high BDNF levels. In addition, less calories mean reduced inflammations and increased levels of antioxidants and BDNF.

The Benefits of a Ketogenic Diet

Aside from caloric restriction, consumption of special fats called ketones is also effective in reducing the risk for brain disease. It heightens metabolic efficiency, stimulates mitochondrial growth, and increases glutathione (a potent, natural antioxidant). Most ketones are produced by the liver but studies show that the brain is also involved in its production, mainly through special cells called astrocytes.

Curcumin and DHA

Curcumin is known for its antibacterial, anti-inflammatory, antifungal, anti-oxidative, and BDNF-producing properties. Docosahexaenoic acid (DHA) is also known for its role as a brain-booster and its contribution to effective brain function. It can even regulate the gene expression for BDNF production. Although our body produces its own share of natural DHA, we also need to consume it from our food sources.

Intellectual Stimulation Bolsters New Networks

Continuously challenging the brain increases retention and enhances neuroplasticity, promoting successful aging and decreasing the risk for brain disorders.

The Antioxidant Hoax

Unlike what modern society believes, our body has the ability to produce natural antioxidants. We are not in dire need of consuming additional ones from external food sources. Even during high levels of oxidative stress, the body can create more protective antioxidants through the activation of the nucleus' specific protein called Nrf2. It also aids the body in detoxification and dampens inflammation.

The "Alzheimer's Gene"

There are several diseases that can be passed down through inheritance such as cystic fibrosis and sickle cell anemia. According to scientists, Alzheimer's might be one too as the increase in the risk of having the disease relates to the presence of a specific gene. However, it still needs further understanding. Having the gene does not entirely seal your fate. It is still up to your mindset and lifestyle.

Chapter 6

Brain Drain

How Gluten Robs You and Your Children's Peace of Mind

Having a high-carb, low-fat diet increases one's chances of having neurological impairments. Since gluten-filled carbs and sugars have become staple food, more destructive effects are seen in people of all ages.

Gluten's Role in Behavioral and Movement Disorders

Attention deficit hyperactivity disorder is one of the most common issues diagnosed in children and is believed to be cured through medications, more specifically, stimulants. However, the extent of the drugs' effects on the brain have not yet been fully studied.

According to Harvard researchers, use of these drugs soared in the past decade where one out of five adults are known to be using them. Most of the patients are prescribed with stimulants which leads to addiction, occasional psychosis, and anxiety. However, we now know that those with celiac disease have higher chances of developing neurological disorders like ADHD. Even gluten sensitivity is linked to anxiety and depression. Basically, we can reduce or limit the

42

symptoms of these disorders by adding DHA and similar supplements on a gluten-free diet.

Apart from narrative proofs from David's patients, the benefits of going gluten-free is starting to become known in the field of science.

Can Autism be Treated with A Gluten-free Diet?

Although it is still too early to conclude on the relationship of gluten sensitivity to autism, it is important to note that both involve inflammation.

Autism is the inflammation of parts of the brain, while celiac disease involves inflammation of the gut. In that sense, going gluten-free might be worth a try, especially since studies show that those with autism have higher levels of inflammatory cytokines in the system which are basically powered by gluten.

Down and Out

By 2020, the World health Organization predicts that depression would be next to heart disease as the largest cause of suffering. At the same time, antidepressants in the pharmaceutical market also continue to rise in number and popularity despite being no more effective than placebo. If you're thinking of taking antidepressants, David encourages you to review the following findings first.

Low Mood and Low Cholesterol

In the previous chapter, it has already been established that cholesterol is indeed good for the brain. In addition, studies show that deficiency in it can cause depression. The same applies to those with bipolar disorder.

The Gluten Blues

The whole thing is basically an overlap of celiac disease with depression and other behavioral or neurological disorders.

Studies show that patients with celiac and gluten sensitivity have increased chances of depression and vice versa. How so? It is because the gut is also called the second brain and produces majority of the body's serotonin.

Without proper nutrition, you'll end up feeling down and irritable more often.

Mental Stability Through Diet

Benefits of going on gluten-free diets even showed results in cases of schizophrenia. Improvements have been observed, especially in the prediction of symptoms.

44

A Fix for the Common Headache?

In the United States, headache is one of the most frequently occurring symptoms. David says that trying a gluten-free diet will be worth the try. You have nothing to lose and besides, those who went on the same diet come out better than before.

Big Headaches in Brief

There are several types of headaches, but migraines are indeed the most common. Although their biochemistry is not yet studied up close, David says that they are caused by gluten sensitivity 90% of the time, no matter what kind it may be. Instead of taking medications that only trigger side effects, David suggests that it would be more worthwhile to focus on your diet and nutritional supplementation instead.

Big Bellies Make for Big Headaches

Researchers from Philadelphia found a relation between abdominal obesity and migraines. This is related to how fat cells produce huge amounts of cytokines which trigger inflammation—the root of headaches.

45

Part II

Grain Brain Rehab

Here you will learn about some of the best ways to improve and, afterwards, maintain your brain health. You'll discover the importance of dietary habits, physical activity, and sleeping habits.

Chapter 7

Dietary Habits for An Optimal Brain

Hello, Fasting, Fats, and Essential Supplements

The human brain is larger than most animal brains. Just so, a larger brain requires more nutrients and energy to function properly. Fortunately, we are given a set of understanding and skills to form plans for the future in terms of food consumption.

The Power of Fasting

One unique characteristic of the human physiology is its ability to utilize other natural energy sources present in the body, namely the ketones. These ketones are broken down stored fats produced from the liver which become alternative sources of energy during starvation.

Compared to glucose, ketones yield greater amounts of energy and slow down cellular destruction. Therefore, fasting allows for the production of greater energy and provides better protection against oxidation, which in turn results to better brain function.

What Fasting and Ketogenic Diets Have in Common

Going on a ketogenic diet mainly involves the

47

consumption of fats and proteins where majority of the calories is obtained, with minimal or no carbohydrate sources. The aim is to increase your dietary fat while burning stored fat in the body.

Grain Brain's low-carb, high-fat diet is similar to fasting in that it lets you tap into your fat stores. Since you do not get sudden boosts in insulin due to fast-digesting carbohydrates, the body has more time to lose or utilize stored fats.

Seven Brain-Boosting Supplements

Modern medicine tends to rely on treatment instead of focusing on prevention. David hopes that with added understanding and awareness of the growing problems on the preservation of mental faculties, future generations of doctors would start switching to prevention-based treatments.

Among the supplements available, DHA is on top. This omega-3 fatty acid composes more than 90% of the brain's omega-3 fats and is found in fish oil and algae.

Another important supplement is the Resveratrol that is known as an antioxidant and inhibitor of fat cell development. It also boosts the immune system and blood flow to the brain, thus improving overall heart and brain health.

We also have turmeric that is proven to have antioxidant and anti-inflammatory properties, reducing brain disease risk.

Probiotics (live microorganisms beneficial to health) are also important for they play a part in processing neurochemical signals and serve as the gut's support system. Through these bacteria, our second brain, the gut, is able to transmit signals through the central nervous system and into the brain.

Reports also show that coconut oil and vitamin D actually support nerve growth while preventing inflammation.

Chapter 8

Genetic Medicine

Jog Your Genes to Build A Better Brain

It was only recently that scientists and medical practitioners alike have discovered the outstanding relationship of the physical and mental health of the human body.

Aside from having physical benefits, exercising also activates the genes that leads to the production of the brain's growth hormones, as previously mentioned in the past chapters as BDNF.

The Magic of Movement

Due to the presence of technology, modern society has shifted into a sedentary lifestyle, ignoring the genome our food-scarce ancestors have formed long ago. By nature, our bodies require physical activity to function properly and time has not changed that.

Experts have found that our brain's sizes grew as the need for higher-thinking skills and for physical activity increased. They also noted this observation in animals (like mice and guinea pigs) as they correlated the brain size to the amount of running done within the lab. Findings even showed that these animal athletes had elevated levels of BDNF, which spurred the growth of brain tissue.

Basically, to develop our brains, we need to exercise and keep the production of our BDNFs going.

Be Nimble and Quick

Preserving the brain consists of five major tasks: getting better blood sugar control, increase in sensitivity to insulin, inflammation control, and boosting BDNF levels through physical exercise.

Researchers from the University of Illinois managed to conclude that the presence of physical activity makes or breaks the production of new brain cells, as shown by their experiment on lab mice. The presence of exercise wheels in the mice's cages made all the difference in the amount of BDNF present in the animals' bloodstreams.

Grow New Networks

Aside from boosting BDNF production, exercise also promotes neurogenesis or the ability of the brain to learn new things.

In addition, it also improves sensitivity to insulin and

51

is an effective anti-inflammatory as it activates the Nrf2 pathways, which activates genes that inhibit inflammation.

It Doesn't Take Much to Make an Impact

Now the question lies on how much and how difficult the exercises have to be to affect brain growth and function.

In a study by researchers from Rush University, risk of Alzheimer's is tripled in people who live the sedentary lifestyle as opposed to those who do daily chores at home. In addition, they also found that the greater the intensity of a physical activity, the greater the decrease in risk of developing the disease.

Chapter 9

Good Night, Brain

Leverage Your Leptin to Rule Your Hormonal Kingdom

In one of David's experiences with a patient of his, enough sleep proved to be a valuable tool in fending off neurological decay. His patient, Samuel, fell victim to Hashimoto's thyroiditis, an autoimmune disease caused by the abnormal attack of the immune system in the thyroid gland.

After getting the gluten sensitivity test, Samuel tested positive and he immediately adopted David's gluten-free diet plan. And it was not long before he started recovering. At the same time, he started getting enough sleep. At first, he thought that it was a side effect of going gluten-free but David says that it most likely wasn't. Instead, it helped Samuel in his recovery.

The Science of Slumber

In recent years, the science behind the concept of sleep has been growing steadily. Research and clinical studies have started discovering that sleep affects the body's biochemistry and processes.

According to their findings, lack of sleep alters the

function of some genes and hormones, which in turn negatively affects the body and the brain. Additional studies even show that only a few of us get enough sleep—and 10% of those who don't suffers from sleep disorders such as chronic insomnia and the like. In addition, people with sleep disorders have higher chances of getting a brain disorder in their later years.

Another topic is our circadian rhythm that basically governs our bodily cycles throughout the 24-hour time period. This includes the regulation of our hormones, temperature, and sleep habits. Disrupting this rhythm will produce negative effects, some of which are the drastic changes in mood, stress, and changes in leptin (the hormone responsible for our body's inflammatory responses).

The Fatter You Are, The Smaller Your Brain

The discovery of leptin spurred greater understanding of the human body and its hormonal system. It handles most of the processes in the hypothalamus and was also found in the most unlikely places: fat cells.

As we know, our fats play a role in other physiological processes aside from being a storage of fuel and an alternative source of energy. The leptin found in our fat cells are tied to our metabolic, behavioral, and hormonal responses to starvation. It controls mammalian metabolism and dictates whether we are hungry or full. Those with lower leptin levels become hungrier and more inclined to eat food high in carbs. And what exactly causes the decrease in leptin? Lack of sleep.

Like insulin, leptin is a vital hormone in the body but if it suddenly goes out of the normal range, it spells trouble for the body and brain. Once your body becomes overloaded with a substance that causes leptin to act over and over, you become leptin resistant—the same thing that happens when you become resistant to insulin. Even if you have more leptin than normal, it won't be able to send signals that you are already full.

Are You Leptin Resistant?

If you are leptin resistant, the *Grain Brain* program can help you.

On the Flip Side: Ghrelin

Another appetite-related hormone is ghrelin. Unlike leptin, this hormone signals when you need to eat. It is secreted by your empty stomach. In studies, ghrelin levels increased significantly in men with inadequate sleep. Basically, when you don't get enough sleep, you get a surge in ghrelin and you get constantly hungry without any actual need for food.

Part III

Say Goodbye to Grain Brain

With the concepts you learned in the previous chapters, you may now start a new healthy life with this section's recommended four-week program. We'll be cutting off the unhealthy carbs through the program's straightforward strategy. David guarantees that once you finish, you will be experiencing changes in every area of your life. You will start feeling that you are in control of your health and feel motivated and encouraged to continuously avoid reverting to your unhealthy lifestyle.

Chapter 10

A New Way of Life

The Four-Week Plan of Action

It won't be surprising at all if you're hesitant to leave your old dietary habits, the carb-filled life, behind. It is indeed hard to change what you were used to since you will start avoiding what you once considered as your staple.

Despite the hurdle of change, David guarantees that this type of lifestyle is doable. Following the program will let you have sharper memory, better sleep, and more energy. If you suffer from any neurological disorder or challenge, such as depression or ADHD, you will start seeing improvements in a matter of weeks.

It is recommended, however, that you check with your physician first especially if you have any health issues like diabetes.

The program includes four goals that you must achieve throughout four weeks:

1. Keeping off carbohydrates and adding supplements in your diet that will help boost your brain.

2. Include a fitness routine in your schedule in case you

still don't have one.

3. Getting enough sleep every week.

4. Setting a new body rhythm aimed towards maintaining and forming healthy habits for a better life.

Every week will be focused on attaining a specific goal and some will require you to consult your doctor for certain tests that will serve as your basis.

Prelude to Week 1: Prepare

Determine Your Baseline

Week 1 will be focusing on your meals and the recommended diet for you. Go to your doctor and have your vitamin D, fasting blood glucose, fructosamine, homocysteine, fasting insulin, C-reactive protein, and hemoglobin A1C tested. Also, take the gluten sensitivity test together with the Cyrex Array 3. Base your results on the baseline and by the end of this program, have them tested all over again.

However, take note that changes with the hemoglobin A1C and the C-reactive protein will show significantly after months of staying on the recommended diet. Whereas your fructosamine levels will show significant change within two to three weeks. Low levels of Vitamin D are also common. It is best to see your doctor for specific recommendations.

Start Your Supplements

In *Grain Brain,* a list of recommended supplements is available, each with the daily dosage recommendation. Although there are specific recommendations for each supplement, David still encourages you to seek advice from your physician.

David also included some notes:

- It is recommended that probiotics be taken on an empty stomach.

- Since turmeric and resveratrol are water-soluble and can be rapidly metabolized, it is best to take them twice daily.

Clear Out Your Kitchen

Start by doing a kitchen inventory. Take out items that you will be eliminating in your diet, such as gluten-filled food and processed starch, carbs, and sugar.

Although some food products may be marked as

gluten-free, David advices that it is still best to keep your eyes peeled since most companies just remove gluten and replace it with another ingredient that is equally unhealthy.

Restock

Stock up on healthy fat, low-sugar fruits, protein, vegetables, herbs, seasonings, and condiments. As much as possible, avoid or limit sweeteners, whole sweet fruits, and wine.

Egg-citing

Today, eggs are one of the most misunderstood food sources in the world as they are viewed to be a source of 'bad cholesterol' that directly builds into blood cholesterol. Contrary to common belief, the dietary cholesterol we get from eggs spurs better cholesterol production and helps improve insulin sensitivity. Eggs also contain essential vitamins, mineral, amino acids, and antioxidants that aid in improving overall health.

Grain Brain's program includes a lot of eggs and David wants you to rid yourself of any ideas in conflict with the true health-benefits they present.

Optional Fast

Before starting on the four-week program, it is

recommended that you fast the day before—although you'll need a continuous supply of water throughout the 24-hour period. According to David, doing so prepares your body for the change and serves as a foundation for the dietary shift.

Week 1: Focus on Food

After sorting the kitchen out, start preparing meals that adhere to certain nutrition guidelines. Unlike the kind of body that runs on carbs, one that's fueled with a high-fat diet will eliminate stress, moodiness, and promote better brain function.

Following the four-week program will give you more room to add moderate carbs in the succeeding months but note that it does not mean that you can revert to your old carb-filled diet. You will be simply providing your body a minimal amount of carbohydrates instead.

For the first three weeks, avoid eating out. Turn your focus away from your cravings and move towards new eating habits. It would also be helpful to keep a food journal where you can take notes on where you're having problems.

Week 2: Focus on Exercise

Make sure that you get some exercise going daily. Research shows that several short exercises throughout the day offer the same benefits as an extensive workout session. Don't forget to include stretching, cardio, and strength training in your routine. If you already have one, then see to it that you increase your workout time by thirty minutes and do it at least five times a week.

Week 3: Focus on Sleep

The minimum number of hours for a healthy sleep is seven hours. Also, remember:

1. Maintain a regular sleeping habit. It will help you maximize the time you slumber and reap the most benefits.

2. Identify and avoid food that hinder sleep like those with caffeine and nicotine.

3. Do not go to bed on an empty or full stomach and eat regularly.

4. Stimulate sleep with the right setting. Dim the lights and find a comfortable spot or position for sleep.

5. Avoid relying on sleeping aids and any drugs that induce sleep. Sleeping naturally is best for you.

Week 4: Put It All Together

By this time, you have most likely adapted to your new routine. But if you are still adjusting, note that it is normal because each person has their own pace. David also presents some helpful advice that can help make the process easier.

Eating Out

By the end of program, try going back to your usual restaurant and order according to what you learned in *Grain Brain*. If the restaurant does not offer any food within the standards of your new diet, treat it as an opportunity to discover other places where you can get your healthy fill.

Provide yourself a few minutes to plan at the start of each week. Set up appointments and check your free schedules. Make priority tasks and note the days when you don't have much time and find out if you can squeeze a little of your routine there.

Before buying, write yourself a list of ingredients. This will keep you on your agenda and prevent you from buying unnecessary products. Avoid the aisles with packaged goods which are more or less processed.

Set your priorities and stick to them. You could help yourself by using apps that help you track your progress or create your meal plans. Sleep and calorie trackers are also available online.

Do not push yourself to the extremes when it comes to your routine. Just be consistent and find what works out for you.

Find what motivates you and cling to it. Things become easier when you feel motivated or when you see a goal ahead of you.

The Balancing Act

According to David, he does not expect you to abstain from eating a pizza or ice cream ever again. However, he hopes that you would try to stick to your new diet and routine 90% of the time.

Chapter 11

Eating Your Way to A Healthy Brain

Meal Plans and Recipes

This chapter presents you with numerous meal ideas and recipes you can include in your diet. But if you want to get creative, you could also use them as references. There isn't much nutrition specifics in any of the recipes since *Grain Brain* only aims to provide you information on what to eat. By following the program, you will be gaining the maximum benefits you can muster for both your body and brain.

David also mentions that most markets are now going organic which gives you more options to choose from. Wild and organic are your best choices for products.

For drinks, it is best to stick with clean water. However, the occasional tea or coffee is perfectly fine, as well as almond milk and red wine. Though again, you shouldn't go for those with added sugars and sweeteners. Also, do your best to avoid drinking coffee late at night.

If you don't have much time to cook for yourself daily, plan your meals and prepare ahead. Learn to use the fridge and reheat wisely.

For snacks, nuts, dark chocolate, raw vegetables, cheese, hard-boiled eggs, and low-sugar fruits are the best choices.

By the way, not all preserved or canned goods are loaded with harmful additives. If you're willing to scrutinize each product on the shelf to find those that meet *Grain Brain*'s requirements, you might get to enjoy added convenience—which is definitely important of you often find yourself having little time for food preparation.

Epilogue

The Mesmerizing Truth

A German physician from Vienna named Franz Anton Mesmer developed a medical treatment he called 'mesmerisim' where he used magnetism to cure people of nervous illnesses. He became infamous in his hometown and in every town he went to after getting banished by those who suspect his methods. As he traveled, he also gained lot of supporters and disciples who can also 'mesmerize' people into being cured.

In the end, his method was found to be a treatment to psychosomatic illnesses which took advantage of his patients' gullible minds. However, this scene is not exactly isolated from what we have in our modern streets of today. A lot of people are fooled into buying brilliantly marketed products known to cure incurable diseases and other health problems.

The past hundred years were a series of proof and disproof on various health topics. What experts categorized as healthy food in the 90s, turned out to be unhealthy today. In this world of dynamics, of change, David wonders if his endeavors would influence people or if he would even

67

achieve his goal of educating people on living the healthy life. He predicts that in the next fifty years or so, more claims would be disproved but with *Grain Brain*, you would know the truth.

The times may be plagued with various diseases that are almost uncurable and we associate the core of our lives with our hearts. However, David says that in believing so, we tend to overlook just how important and big the role of our minds in keeping our body healthy. But with *Grain Brain*, you are now aware and responsible for your mental health.

About the Author

David Perlmutter is an outstanding neurologist who has published and lectured about his views on neurological diseases. He has received awards for his research and appeared on television. He is also a member of the American College of Nutrition. He is a father of two and lives with them and his wife in Naples, Florida.

Conclusion

Unbeknownst to many, brain diseases are also influenced by our nutrition and lifestyle choice. It does not befall us by chance.

During the period when our ancestors lived, technology was far from what we have now and everyday was a struggle for food. They had no processed products and they relied on the nutrients they get from edible plants and the animals they successfully hunted. A man can die form an infection or from a predator lurking in the shadows.

Medicine has continued to develop and save lives all-around the world. But in recent years, people with neurological diseases or disorders has significantly increased and slow-acting diseases like Alzheimer's continue to plague the human society. And the culprit lies in our everyday living. More specifically, in the food we eat.

Grain Brain tackled a major problem and source—inflammation, which is essentially the process by which the body fights off intruders by neutralizing toxins or sending killer cells to the affected area. With brain diseases though, inflammatory cytokine chemicals harm normal brain cells. And since the brain has no pain receptors, you won't know there is something wrong until it's too late. And a major cause for brain inflammation is gluten sensitivity.

Gluten sensitivity is not limited to celiac disease. You can be sensitive to gluten without realizing it unless you get yourself tested.

Aside from gluten, carbohydrates should be minimized from your diet since it promotes inflammation. Our liver can provide enough for our needs and having a surplus leads to more stored fats, which in turn halts the breakdown of naturally stored fats in the body. However, fats are actually good for the body for they help in regulating the immune system. Cholesterol is also one misunderstood topic. Contrary to common belief, eating cholesterol-rich food does not translate into having cholesterol that clogs your arteries. In fact, the brain consists of cholesterol which helps build better connections.

The real culprit to brain decay are carbohydrates which are made up of sugars. As you've learned, sugars are detrimental to health and increases the risk for obesity. Excess intake of sugar triggers the over-production of insulin, which leads to increased storage of fats. And that in turn stimulates the inflammatory pathways, bringing us back to the major cause of harm to the brain: inflammation.

71

However, it is not entirely too late for you can change your lifestyle and thus develop a healthier mind and body. Contrary to common knowledge, the brain can regenerate. Neurogenesis is slowly finding its way into the scientific and medical world. To promote neurogenesis, you will need to be physically active, reduce your caloric intake, increase fat and protein intake, and avoid carbs, sugars, and processed products.

You can also try fasting to help your body burn the stored fat. But do note that going on a low-carb, high-fat diet does the same. Also, don't forget to get enough DHA, Vitamin D, sleep, and exercise. Follow *Grain Brain*'s four-week program and recommended diet to finally live a healthier life and have a better brain.

Final Thoughts

Hey! Did you enjoy this book? We sincerely hope you thoroughly enjoyed this short read and have gotten immensely valuable insights that will help you in any areas of your life.

Would it be too greedy if we ask for a review from you?

It takes 1 minute to leave 1 review to possibly influence 1 more person's decision to read just 1 book which may change their 1 life. Your 1 minute matters and we value it and thank you so much for giving us your 1 minute. If it sucks, just say it sucks. Period.

FREE BONUS

P.S. Is it okay if we overdeliver?

Here at Abbey Beathan Publishing, we believe in overdelivering way beyond our reader's expectations. Is it okay if we overdeliver?

Here's the deal, we're going to give you an extremely valuable cheatsheet of "Accelerated Learning". We've partnered up with Ikigai Publishing to present to you the exclusive bonus of "Accelerated Learning Cheatsheet"

What's the catch? We need to trust you... You see, we want to overdeliver and in order for us to do that, we've to trust our reader to keep this bonus a secret to themselves. Why? Because we don't want people to be getting our exclusive accelerated learning cheatsheet without even buying our books itself. Unethical, right?

Ok. Are you ready?

Simply Visit this link: http://bit.ly/acceleratedcheatsheet

We hope you'll enjoy our free bonuses as much as we've enjoyed preparing it for you!

Free Bonus #2: Free Book Preview of Summary:
Give and Take
The Book at a Glance

All throughout our life, we interact with people who have different reciprocity styles. A person may be a giver, a taker, or a matcher. A taker is someone who is concerned of his own interests. They take more than what they give. A matcher is someone who gives the same amount he or she receives. On the other hand, a giver is someone who is concerned of others' well-being. Givers can be classified as selfless givers or otherish givers. Selfless givers are more likely to be doormats and pushovers because they sacrifice their own interests to help others. They are most likely to fail and end up at the bottom. On the other hand, otherish givers are givers who are concerned of others but are also concerned of his or her own interests. They are most likely to be successful.

Otherish givers are proof that assertiveness is not the only factor to get to the top. They show people that giving can be a factor of success. Furthermore, they prove that we don't need to be selfish to achieve success. Giving provides a lot of benefits. It can build networks which you could get access to new information. It can also build long-lasting relationships.

This book aims to inform the readers how givers rise to the top. The author wants to prove that givers are not pushovers and doormats and they are as competent as takers and matchers.

Moreover, the book shows that takers and matchers can shift to the giver direction through helping in the community they belong in. The book does not only intend to inform the readers how giving can help people achieve success but also to encourage readers to be givers to have a richer purpose, more lasting impact, and more success.

The first five chapters of the book contain the principles of giver success, showing how and why givers become successful. The five chapters also include how givers interact in networking, collaborating, evaluating, and influencing.

The last three chapters of the book discuss the benefits and costs of giving. These chapters emphasize how givers manage to avoid burnout and to avoid being pushovers and doormats. These chapters prove that giving can make you happier and live longer.

Chapter 1: Good Returns describes the three reciprocity styles. The chapter discusses the advantages and disadvantages of each reciprocity styles in various situations. Moreover, the chapter includes how each reciprocity style rise to the top. It emphasizes that givers can be successful, too. Stories of David Hornik and Abraham Lincoln were used as an example of success stories of famous givers.

Chapter 2: The Peacock and the Panda discusses how givers, takers, and matchers build their networks and how important networking is in achieving success. The chapter also includes how to spot a taker disguised as a giver, how social media makes it easier for people to identify a person's reciprocity style, how important are weak ties and dormant ties in rising to the top, and how doing a favor that would only take for five minutes or less for someone can be rewarding.

Chapter 3: The Ripple Effect describes how collaboration can put a person in an advantage. It emphasizes how takers and givers differ in a team. It also explains why most givers are not known and how takers dominate the spotlight. Givers do not thirst on taking credits. They usually give away the credit. Moreover, it emphasizes the importance of being empathetic with people.

Chapter 4: Finding the Diamond in the Rough emphasizes how givers recognize potential in people. It also includes how high expectations from others motivate people to perform better. Moreover, the chapter describes how givers hone a person with an untapped potential and when do givers give up a bad talent.

Chapter 5: The Power of Powerless Communication emphasizes how powerless communication can help givers achieve success. Forms of powerless communication are discussed in this chapter. It also includes how useful powerless communication is in presenting, selling, persuading, and negotiating. Also, it emphasizes the importance of modesty in earning respect and prestige.

Chapter 6: The Art of Motivation Maintenance discusses how givers avoid burnout. The chapter also discusses how selfless givers differ from otherish givers. Furthermore, it discusses how do otherish givers rise to the top and why do selfless givers end up at the bottom. Furthermore, the chapter describes otherish strategies such as chunking and the 100-hour rule of volunteering that you could apply in your work or life.

Chapter 7: Chump Change describes how otherish givers avoid becoming doormats and pushovers and how selfless givers overcome the doormat effect. The chapter includes how otherish strategies such as sincerity screening, generous tit for tat, and advocating for others can help avoid the doormat effect.

Chapter 8: The Scrooge Shift discusses how belonging to a community can tilt people into the giver direction. The chapter describes the principle of optimal distinctiveness, uncommon commonality and reciprocity ring.

Chapter 9: Out of The Shadows emphasizes that givers can be on top and there is no reason to hide giver values. It emphasizes that givers are not weak and naïve unlike what people perceive them to be.

"Actions for Impact" presents a set of practical actions the reader can apply in his or her work or life to live by the principle of giving. It includes strategies and habits of successful givers that the reader can apply.

This book will make you reconsider your perception of success. This book is for everyone, regardless of your reciprocity style. If you are a selfless giver, you may gain insights on how to become otherish and make your way to the top. If you are a matcher, you will be surprised at how you can help others without compromising your own success. If you are a taker, you may be tempted to shift into the giver direction. You'll realize that selfishness will not get you to the top. However, it probably won't work if you give just because you want to succeed.

Chapter 1

Good Returns

The Dangers and Rewards of Giving More Than What You Get

In all courses of life, people can identify themselves as givers or takers. Givers are generous people who prioritize the well-being of others than their own well-being. They give more than what they get in return. On the other hand, takers are competitive and self-focused people. They want to be better than others and take more than what they give. However, some people are matchers. They strike a balance between giving and taking. When they give something, they seek something in return. Nonetheless, you might find yourself shifting from one reciprocity style to another.

Each reciprocity style has its own pros and cons. Studies have found that givers are more likely to be at the bottom of the success ladder. Prioritizing others' success and sacrificing their own becomes a disadvantage to givers. Because givers care and trust too much, they are more likely to be less powerful and dominant. If you think takers or matchers are the ones on top of the success ladder, you are wrong. Surprisingly, it's the givers again.

For deeper understanding, the author used David Hornik's story to illustrate how givers might be at a disadvantage but somehow managed to be successful. Danny Shader's idea was to provide a solution to the problem of Americans who have trouble purchasing online because they don't have a bank account or credit card. Shader thought Hornik would be a great investor for his pitch since Hornik's specialization is on Internet companies. Hornik liked Shader's idea but he gave Shader the option to explore more investors before settling with him. He was hoping Shader would choose him and even gave Shader a list of references to prove his competence and trustworthiness. Unfortunately, Shader chose another investor because he thought Hornik was not a challenging investor.

Shader eventually regretted his decision of letting go of the opportunity to work with Hornik. He invited Hornik to become one of his investors, which Hornik gladly accepted. Shader discovered how competent and dedicated Hornik as an investor. He overlooked Hornik's competence and dedication because he thought Hornik was too giving. From then on, Shader recommended Hornik to other investors. It was a win-win situation for both of them. Hornik might have been at a disadvantage as a giver but he eventually became successful because of the same reason.

Givers and takers have different kind of successes. When a taker succeeds, rivals would try to pull them down. In contrast, when givers succeed, people support them instead of pulling them down. The path to success is smoother when you don't have enemies who are trying to pull you down. Some people think that givers are pushovers in politics. However, some politicians who are givers are successful in the field. An example of which is Abraham Lincoln.

Abraham Lincoln is known as one of the best leaders of the world. He was a leader who puts the well-being of the nation before his own well-being. He aspired to be the Clinton of Illinois despite of him being a farm worker. He lacked credentials to be qualified as a politician but he still grabbed the chance to run as a Senator. Sadly, he lost and put up a business which eventually failed, leaving him with debt. At twenty-five years old, he tried his luck and ran for a seat in the state legislature. Fortunately, he won and served the legislature while earning a degree in law. At age forty-five, he tried his luck once again and ran for a seat in the Senate.

He was the most popular candidate, consistently on top of the poll. He competed with James Shields and Lyman Trumbull who were more qualified than him. Joel Matteson entered the picture and swept off the popularity poll, putting Lincoln at second. Lincoln doubted his ability and decided to withdraw from the race. He asked his supporters to vote for Trumbull instead since he and Trumbull shared the same values. His only aim was to prevent Matteson for winning because he knew Matteson has engaged himself in questionable practices. He didn't want such leader to lead his beloved nation.

Trumbull won a seat in the Senate at the expense of Lincoln. People were worried that Lincoln was not capable of making tough political decisions when he withdrew his candidacy. However,

Lincoln did not give up on pursuing his interest to serve the nation. He ran for the Senate again, four years after Trumbull had won. Lincoln's sacrifice had paid off when Trumbull rooted for him when he ran again. As we all know, Lincoln eventually become the President of the United States. He appointed his rivals as his cabinet members because he believed the nation needs leaders who are educated, knowledgeable, and experienced. He did not think of himself when he appointed his rivals. Instead, he put the nation's well-being first before his own by appointing men who are worthy to serve the nation and for its betterment.

People tend to overlook the advantages of being a giver. They think givers would not make it to the top because they are weak and naïve. Seemingly, givers become successful in the long run. Givers can succeed in whatever field they choose. However, givers are hesitant to show their giver tendencies because they are afraid to be judged as naïve and weak. Givers can be excellent influencers, too. They help others succeed which eventually establishes a relationship with others. Givers have unique approaches when interacting with other people in networking, collaborating, evaluating, and influencing. Each of the four domains will be discussed thoroughly in the next chapters.

SUMMARY:

Grant

ABBEY BEATHAN

Text Copyright © Abbey Beathan

Legal & Disclaimer

The information contained in this book is not designed to replace or take the place of any form of medicine or professional medical advice. The information in this book has been provided for educational and entertainment purposes only.

The information contained in this book has been compiled from sources deemed reliable, and it is accurate to the best of the Author's knowledge; however, the Author cannot guarantee its accuracy and validity and cannot be held liable for any errors or omissions. Changes are periodically made to this book. You must consult your doctor or get professional medical advice before using any of the suggested remedies, techniques, or information in this book. Images used in this book are not the same as of those of the actual book. This is a totally separate and different entity from that of the original book titled: "Grant"

Upon using the information contained in this book, you agree to hold harmless the Author from and against any damages, costs, and expenses, including any legal fees potentially resulting from the application of any of the information provided by this guide. This disclaimer applies to any damages or injury caused by the use and application, whether directly or indirectly, of any advice or information presented, whether for breach of contract, tort, negligence, personal injury, criminal intent, or under any other cause of action.

You agree to accept all risks of using the information presented inside this book. You need to consult a professional medical practitioner in order to ensure you are both able and healthy enough to participate in this program.

Table of Contents

The Book at a Glance

Ulysses S. Grant is at once one of the most revered heroes in American history and one of its most tragic; a robust and seemingly indestructible public figure who descended into a life of alcoholism, failed business ventures, and a painful cancer-addled demise. He shepherded the North's Union Army in a brutal American War, winning praises from the North for his skilled generalship and from his Southern rivals for his compassion and even-handedness as the victor in a terrible war.

He then won a two-term presidency in a nation that was not quite "formed" with many of its institutions still in the incipient stages and just "finding its legs." His heroism and grit in leading the Union army through his quiet confidence is an enduring image - standing proudly as among the biggest heroes in the pantheon of American presidents. The great American poet Walt Whitman, a big fan of Grant said that he was burdened with, "a task of peace, more difficult than the war itself," and he acquitted himself excellently on both counts.

Through the passage of time however, especially in the age of endless psychoanalysis, his reputation has suffered. Many have glossed over his accomplishments as general and president, and instead focused on his drinking and terrible final days when facing mortality; he was not exactly the face of proper decorum and politeness. The loss of his fortune to a *Ponzi Scheme* huckster, which ruined him financially, put his judgement into question.

The fact that he presided in the Gilded Age of robber barons led many to accuse him of being a carpet bagger, after he brutally imposed a brutal martial government on the Southern whites. But he was also attacked as too lenient on the vanquished, speaking volumes of history's fickleness with the man.

Ron Chernow's massive volume tackles every dimension of the man, but eventually digs in with the camp that argues for his greatness. To the author, Grant is heroic even during his failures including his often and pitiful surrender to alcohol. His failings pale miserably to the pride that Americans take in his exploits starting from an uncertain plebe in West Point, through his battlefield heroics, his tortured presidency, an unofficial ambassador, and a tortured man nearing his death, wracked with incurable pain and an inevitable fate.

The author Ron Chernow is a Pulitzer Prize winning best-selling author who is known for his extensive biographies of historical figures. He wrote comprehensive biographies of George Washington, Alexander Hamilton, and John D. Rockefeller. His books on Hamilton and the House of Morgan were turned into full-length documentary features.

Chernow received his Literature degree from Yale University. A lifetime New Yorker, he lives in New York City with his wife and child.

PART ONE: A LIFE OF STRUGGLE

ONE: Country Bumpkin

Ulysses S. Grant was born and christened Hiram Ulysses Grant to Hannah Simpson and Jesse Grant on April 27, 1822, in Pleasant Point Ohio. Jesse was a tanner who was the son of Noah Grant who turned to alcoholism and died a poor man. Jesse was also an abolitionist who converted himself from an uneducated orphan to a successful tanner. He was a loquacious political animal while his wife Hannah was a quiet and proper girl. Ulysses apparently took after his mother's quiet inner strength, a trademark trait throughout his life.

Jesse Grant worked as a farmhand for three years before the family of an Ohio Supreme Court judge, George Tod, who Jesse worked for, found a liking for him and taught him how to read. Jesse found his calling in tannery and started a business in the craft. After he married Hannah, he moved the family to Georgetown Ohio, where Ulysses Grant began his formal schooling. The Grant household percolated with political commentary, and before long, Jesse Grant himself found himself campaigning and running for various offices, but always ending up short. They moved again later on to an even smaller Bethel, a move up the socio-economic ladder where Jesse's tanning business would prosper even more.

Once staunch supporters of Andrew Jackson, Jesse and Hannah denounced the president for his overreaching use of executive power. Jesse had joined the new Whig Party that had spun off from the Democratic Party. Jesse was a big fan of Whig leader Henry Clay, who endorsed the American systems of national bank high tariffs, and a system of internal improvements. This orientation was strongly apparent in Ulysses Grant's presidency later on.

The Whigs' adherence to a strong religious and moral code reflected in how the Grants ran their household. Ulysses combined his mother's Sphinx-like countenance with unshakeable moral fortitude. He was not very garrulous and, according to most, not physical striking despite his sparkling blue eyes. He spoke of no lofty dreams unlike many famous men in their youth. His only passion was horses – about which he learned the details of how to raise and train them. He had absolutely no desire to follow in his father's footsteps in tannery, which he found absolutely disgusting.

After sending Ulysses to a private academy in Kentucky, Jesse Grant, without consulting with Ulysses, sent his son's name for consideration to attend the United States Military

Academy at West Point. Ulysses was appalled to learn what his father had done and initially resisted him, but to no avail. Ulysses knew anyway that he would not meet the stringent entrance requirements of the academy. The entrance test was notoriously difficult and being of small stature, he was sure that he was not cut out to be a soldier.

TWO: The Darling Young Lieutenant

A seventeen year-old Ulysses Grant, at 5'2' and 117 pounds left for his West Point appointment. He spent five days in Philadelphia on the way to the academy, and secretly wished that an accident would befall him so that he did not have to continue on his trip. When he arrived at West Point, a clerical error caused his name to be registered as Ulysses S. Grant (the "S." not meaning anything), but he just decided to go with it so as not to create any disruption.

Grant was surprised to pass the entrance exam since 25% of applicants failed the test. At 17, he was physically among the smallest members of the 1839 freshman class, but his size did nothing to diminish his performance. The life at West Point was difficult with cadets having to get up at 5 a.m. followed by a rigorous schedule of classes and physical drills. Despite getting less than stellar grades, he was greatly respected among his classmates for his demeanor and diligence.

 Grant learned a great deal of military theory and tactics while at West Point, which he applied successfully in future battles during the Civil War. He became a voracious reader and displayed outstanding skills in topography and mathematics.

He also met a lot of his future confederate rivals at the school, including Thomas Jonathan "Stonewall" Jackson; and he said that his knowledge of his peers helped him immensely in dealing with them in war time. He met many other future generals but he became closest to William Tecumseh Sherman, who would serve under him in the Union Army during the war. Other future generals that he encountered at West Point would be future allies and foes: Simon Bolivar Buckner, Robert Lee, and others.

In June 1843, in a day that he considered among the happiest in his life, Grant graduated twenty-first out of a class of thirty-nine, which translated to being in the class' top quartile if the cadets who dropped out during the four years are considered. His professor in mathematics saw great promise in the young Grant and offered him to return to West Point as an assistant professor in the subject.

The diminutive Grant did not get a respectable reception upon returning to his hometown, and was somewhat relieved to be assigned to Jefferson Barracks in Missouri, at the time the largest military outpost in the United States.

While at Jefferson Barracks, he was introduced by Fred Dent, his West Point roommate to Dent's sister, Julia who was five years Grant's junior. Julia was lovestruck by Grant, now the strapping young West Point graduate, and Grant, for the first time in his life, fell in love. While Julia's mother Ella approved of the young officer, her father Col. Frederick Dent was vehemently opposed to their relationship. The elder Dent felt that a fellow in the Army could not adequately provide for the security and needs of his daughter. Julia, who was somewhat chubby and afflicted with "strabismus" or a congenital lazy eye, did not exactly draw a lot of interest from men, and her father encouraged her to attend as many gatherings with eligible men where she might meet a future spouse.

In choosing Julia to be the object of his affection, Grant was making a Faustian bargain in which he would be getting a father-in-law that had as much bluster as his own father, Jesse. To make matters worse, Frederick Dent was a slaveowner who had political views in direct opposition to Jesse Grant. It seemed that Ulysses S. Grant, future president of the United States was cursed to a life of perpetual adolescence in which he would struggle to assert himself without getting slapped down.

THREE: Rough and Ready

In 1844, Grant's first foray in military action was a result of what Grant later on considered an imperialist adventure to annex Texas from Mexico. It was also during this time that he entered into a frenetic letter-writing arrangement with Julia and his family. Democrat James Polk who made the annexation of Texas a main campaign platform, narrowly beat Henry Clay in the presidential elections; and after lame duck president John Tyler signed the congressional resolution for the annexation of Texas, war with Mexico was imminent.

Fully aware that he was going to be deployed to war, Grant returned to St. Louis to ask Col. Dent for permission to marry his daughter. Dent refused, but promised Grant that if he and Julia still felt the same about each other one or two years hence, then he might reconsider and bless their marriage. Disappointed but unbowed, Grant marched off to face his military duties. His commander would be Zachary Taylor, another future president whose nickname was "Old Rough and Ready." Unlike Grant, who idolized him, he was not a West Point graduate, but had been a professional soldier since he was eighteen.

Grant was stationed in Corpus Christi, Texas with his regiment by September 1845. In a letter to Julia from there, Grant did not appear to be opposed to the war, but saw instead that the Mexicans that he observed in the area would be better off under the U.S. form of government. Still, Grant was hopeful that some diplomatic solution could be reached so that he could come back to Julia and work on getting married to her. But reality soon took over – war was imminent and he had to spend more time in Corpus Christi, by then a growing town that had many of the immoral features of a lax town financed by military money.

On May, 1845 Taylor marched his army to Palo Alto, where he faced a much larger Mexican army. The Americans, however, routed the Mexicans with their superior artillery, but not after Grant discovered two things. First, war was grisly business. He had blood and brains spattered on him as his comrades were blown apart by cannonballs. Second, he found that he was preternaturally calm and cool under fire, as if the ravages of war anesthetized him. This was echoed publicly and privately by men who fought with him. They were amazed not only by his coolness under fire, but also by his quick thinking and decision-making.

When Taylor moved further South to Monterey and closer to

101

the Mexican border, Grant was assigned to be the acting assistant quartermaster as a testament to his efficiency. Grant, however, wanted none of this because he wanted to be at the front lines to fight with his men instead of being a backline support functionary to the fighting infantry. This posting made him a much better general however, because of the exposure to wartime logistics. His West Point sponsor, Ohio congressman Thomas Hamer, saw this in Grant when he visited the troops in Monterey and commented on Grant's bright future in the army.

FOUR: The Son of Temperance

In 1848 Grant was able to arrange a visit to St. Louis to meet the Dents, where they had a summer home. After four years of a long-distance engagement, Grant was eager to be with Julia again. At the time of his visit, Frederick Dent had a number of financial setbacks that weakened his resolve to keep Grant from marrying his daughter and he finally consented to their marriage.

They finally got married on August 22, 1848, and both sides of their families had various reasons to skip the wedding. Grant was thrust into his own little civil war in which Julia's family of slave-owning Democrats despised Ulysses' brood of abolitionists. When Grant finally introduced the new bride to his parents, they treated her with civility, which the proper Julia reciprocated with her ladylike charm.

Frederick Dent however, decided one last time to drive a wedge between his daughter and Grant. Frederick requested Grant to leave Julia behind on his next posting assignment, a prospect that Julia momentarily considered given that she had never been away from her family her entire life. They left for his posting in Detroit just as his former commander Zachary Taylor won the presidency of the United States (he would die in less than two years from a mysterious stomach ailment).

Upon his arrival in Detroit, he found out that there was already a quartermaster for the barracks. While he filed a protest, he was relocated to Sackets Harbor in New York, a cold and desolate place. As winter approached, Grant with his usual take-charge attitude organized his post even as he worried on how Julia would manage with such a bleak posting. Julia however, acquitted herself wonderfully and made a cozy home for herself and her husband.

On March 2, 1849 Grant won his protest and was re-assigned to Detroit and the newly married couple had to re-settle in a new place again. It was in Detroit where they grew even closer as Julia once again proved her mettle in keeping a household for her husband who was growing fonder of his new wife by the day. Many observers agreed that Julia grant was the light and life of Ulysses.

Julia got pregnant in 1849 and decided to have her baby in St. Louis under the watchful eyes of her family. On May 30, 1849, she gave birth to their first son, Frederick Dent Grant, with Ulysses not appreciating that his first born had been named after his contrarian father-in-law.

The separation from Julia and their child, coupled with the

lack of challenging work, exposed Grant to alcohol and he would experience his first challenges with drunkenness. He confided with his pastor in Detroit about it and acknowledged his weakness with the bottle. While he was never cavalier about his problem, alcoholism would hound him all throughout most of his life, especially since being inebriated subjected him to erratic behavior, which did not sit well with many of his comrades and superiors.

He found solace in the lectures of John B. Gough, a pioneer in the temperance movement. He was so encouraged by Gough's sincerity and will that Grant himself founded a lodge of the Sons of Temperance in Sackets Harbor.

In September 1851, Julia travelled to Sackets Harbor with their baby, but had to leave again a few months later when Ulysses was ordered to travel to California via Panama. He would not see his family again for two years, which drove him to depression. On the crowded steamship *Ohio*, he fell off the wagon and he started to drink again.

When he arrived in Panama, Grant was appalled to find that the contractor the Army hired to provide pack animals and supplies decided to sell their goods to a higher bidder. Despite this tremendous setback, Grant displayed what would be his soon to be famous "split metabolism" -

Drawing on a reserve of inner strength, grace under fire, and resolve. He also displayed a lot of sympathy and empathy for American Indians and especially Negro slaves, a sentiment that would significantly affect American policy towards blacks down the road.

His excellent military skills notwithstanding, he was a bust in almost everything else he tried. He was too guileless to prosper in personal financial dealings, in which he was perceived as a simpleton and he was repeatedly cheated out of funds, which left him destitute. He also did not have a flair for business, where every one of his business ventures before the Civil War failed. Separated from his family and completely lost and clueless without military work, Grant got a break when he was promoted to Captain after the death of an officer. He was reassigned to Fort Humboldt, another remote outpost in Northern California, where his personal life and military career would change dramatically.

FIVE: Payday

In January 1844, Grant arrived in Humboldt, California, where being a military captain without being in battle was depressing to the young soldier starved for action. He did not get along with his commanding officer, Robert Buchanan, and his alcohol demons began to rear their ugly heads again. He was caught drunk one day and was asked by Buchanan to resign from his post at Humboldt. After he formally got his promotion to captain, he quit and left Humboldt.

Julia was a fierce protector of her husband, and sin or no sin, she argued that her husband was not a drunkard. Without telling Julia that he had resigned from his post, he went to San Francisco to try out his business acumen and hopefully make a living. Instead of prospering, Grant was constantly being duped by other people who figured him out as a simpleton in financial and business issues.

He ended up penniless in San Francisco and had to rely on the generosity of former friends who were shocked at his state of affairs. He was able to somehow cajole his friends for passage to New York and left California in June, 1854. When he finally was able to see his parents after years of separation, his gaunt and somewhat wild appearance shocked them and led them to suspect that maybe the rumors they had heard about his drinking had some basis.

Lacking for work, Grant was forced to swallow his pride and agreed to work on a farm acreage near St. Louis owned by his father-in-law, Frederick Dent. While Ulysses and his family lived on the edges of poverty, Julia did not lose faith in her husband - even if almost everybody else did. She was confident that Ulysses was destined for bigger things and doted on him. She took care of the family finances, knowing about Grant's acknowledged handicap in handling money. He reciprocated by exhibiting the utmost affection for his wife and children. Around his family, Grant was never observed to have taken alcohol although he had taken up another unhealthy habit, smoking.

While he toiled away on his father-in-law's farm, the slavery issue was reaching its boiling point at the verge of rending the country in two. There was a philosophical and economic divide between the North and the South that focused on the treatment of slaves. It came to a head when Supreme Court Chief Justice Roger Taney handed down the infamous *Dred Scott* decision, essentially saying that a black man could not be considered a citizen because he was an inferior being. Grant increasingly despised slavery and found himself at odds with the Dents and to some extent, Julia, who herself had four young black slaves at her disposal.

The 1857 economic depression added to Grant's worries as income from his farm shrank significantly just as his fourth child was being born. The overlapping problems led to migraine headaches at least once a month. Eventually he had to give up his adventure in farming and hit the streets of St. Louis, once again a jobless man. He was able to find employment, but even Julia acknowledged that her husband plainly did not possess certain skills outside those related to the army. In one of the worst moments of his life, he had no choice but to work for his father's business if he didn't want his family to go hungry.

PART TWO: A LIFE OF WAR

SIX: The Store Clerk

Ulysses Grant and his family arrived in Galena, Illinois, in April, 1860 intent on starting a new life. He arrived looking older and stooped as he tried to ready himself for a civilian life that history would eventually reveal was never meant for him. Outside of the military, daily work was drudgery for Grant as he displayed little or no business sense. He ended up working for his father and brother, Orvil, both of whom did not hide their contempt for Julia, and to some extent, her children. Orvil was particularly irked by Ulysses' doting of his children, especially the younger Jesse. Grant defended his family against all critics, and by all accounts, led a comfortable and quiet life in Galena, attending a Methodist church, and pretty much keeping to themselves.

The usually withdrawn Ulysses lit up, however, when he talked about his military exploits, and his gift for conversation about the military and politics made him an interesting figure among those who visited his family's leather store. Politics was a very hot topic at the time, when the Republican Party was at odds during an election year, and when the Southern states were grumbling about keeping slavery intact while the abolitionists like Jesse Grant, pulled at the other end of the argument.

In November 1860, Abraham Lincoln won the presidency of the United States with only 40% of the popular vote. In a portent of things to come, Lincoln did not win a single vote in the Southern states as his name did not even appear in the ballot. While Ulysses Grant did not meet the residency requirements to vote in Illinois, he found that his political views had aligned very closely with that of Lincoln – the abolition of slavery. But Grant would find a new ally in Congressman Elihu Washburne in whose district the Grants lived.

The first political shot at the bow of the North was when South Carolina voted to secede from the Union, which only deepened Grant's pro-abolitionist fervor. While many thought that the South did not have it in them to mount a war against the North, Grant believed that there was enough fervor for a war to be engaged. He mistakenly thought that such a war would be short-lived, as he also thought that the North possessed overwhelming advantages in military manpower and materials.

In January 1861, five more states seceded, and the following month, the seceding states drafted Jefferson Davis as their interim president. On April 12, 1861 the Civil War officially started when Confederate general Pierre Gustave Toutant-Beauregard ordered the shelling of Fort Sumter near Charleston, South Carolina, that forced the surrender of Union forces. Ironically not a single soul was lost in the first Civil War skirmish belying the horrendous casualty levels that the War would have in the next four years.

Ulysses Grant, not yet quite thirty-nine years old, itched to be re-enlisted and fight for the Union. He wore the new purpose and determination in his face and demeanor. He joined the first group of Galena volunteers that he immediately regaled and impressed with his encyclopedic knowledge of military matters, leading to the enlistment of many men during the first meeting.

Despite his knowledge, politics and his reputation for drunkenness prevented him from getting an early military commission. He was not one for jockeying for position or currying any favors and did not bemoan this initial failure to get a military rank. All he wanted to do was to fight for the Union, period. All he could get initially was a back-office administrative job that he accepted grudgingly. But Elihu Washburne continued

to goad a hesitant Illinois governor Richard Yates, and Grant finally got the military commission that he so dearly coveted.

SEVEN: The Quiet Man

Grant did not waste any time making his views known on slavery to everyone including his father-in-law. When he finally got an appointment from Governor Yates as colonel of a regiment in Illinois, it seemed like he was born again, his spirits soaring now that he was soon to be in his element. Two things immediately struck those who first laid their eyes on him: First, that a short, slight, and unassuming young man did not project the authority warranted of a military leader, but second and most important, he had a quiet inner strength, which prevented anger over sleights towards him. Observers were also impressed by his candor and his charitable nature.

The fuel for his commitment to master his military craft was his loathing of slavery, which went against the very grain of his being that ached for fairness and opportunity for everyone, no matter what the color of his skin was.

In his first couple of military assignments, he displayed the qualities that would make him the transcendent military leader of his time. He knew how to get into the minds of his opposing commanders, and his swift decision-making that was coupled with his philosophy of striking the enemy without delay. To him, delays were much worse than making the wrong decision.

As he was just beginning to flex his military muscles, the Union suffered devastating and unexpected losses in the first Manassas ("Bull Run") battle in Virginia. Almost in a state of panic, Abraham Lincoln expanded his military by a million soldiers through the draft which necessitated the minting of new officers. Largely through the intervention of Illinois congressman Elihu Washburne, Grant was given a brigadier general commission, and was now suddenly in command of four thousand men. The promotion made no one happier than Julia Grant, who wasted no time in trumpeting the honor bestowed on her long-suffering husband.

As a brigadier-general, Ulysses Grant continued to display the no-flash, no-nonsense brand of leadership that endeared him to his soldiers. He kept his composure as he suffered through seemingly irrational re-assignments that were borne out of political exigencies rather than military need. Grant, who never mixed politics with military action, took it all in with dignified resignation, even if he disagreed with decisions made above his pay-grade.

In his first major assignment as brigadier-general, Grant was

115

sent to Missouri to chase down a Confederate general's regiment that was harassing Union troops in the swamps in the state. As a prelude to this and other engagements, he set up office and made a fortunate hire as an assistant, John Rawlins, a lawyer whose rhetoric had bowled Grant over in one of his recruitment events in Galena. It would turn out that one of Rawlins' most important jobs was to monitor and help prevent Grant's occasional descents to drunkenness. Rawlins was one of the very few people that the intensely private Grant would allow into his cloistered world, and both men would be the best of friends all their lives. Rawlins would be the conscience and moral guide of the man who would turn out to possess the greatest military mind of the era while having no military experience or training.

EIGHT: Twin Forts

Grant was next assigned to conquer Paducah, a key Kentucky town controlled by the rebels that was a crucial springboard for securing Confederate territory. He placed his military career on the line by pre-empting his commander John Fremont and blitzing the city before the Confederates arrived. In a precursor to future engagement with civilian populations, he allayed the fears of the frightened civilian population that he considered them fellow citizens, and therefore would not harm them in any way.

Awash with his "victory," he had Julia join him in Paducah, where it appeared that she had converted her allegiance to the Union side. When Fremont was dismissed by President Lincoln after unilaterally declaring martial law in Missouri, Grant took over his command and took over Belmont and Columbus using a quick strike strategy that would be a trademark of his offensive style. For Grant, timing and speed was much more important than having the troops exactly in place. Taking Belmont was his baptism of fire, and he showed preternatural coolness in the midst of the daring and swift nature of his actions. The Belmont victory however was not a complete one and exposed one of his weaknesses – he failed to anticipate countermoves by his opponents, leaving his forces susceptible to counter-attack.

In the interregnum, Grant sought to clean up his troops' camps of corruption and slovenliness. He also stridently beat back his father's attempts to capitalize on his name by trying to curry political and business favors. In November 1861, Fremont was replaced by Maj. Gen. Henry Halleck, a significant development that would not only impact Grant's military career, but Halleck's as well. Both men were not made of the same cloth, which created many problems between them. Halleck was an armchair general with a lot of theoretical knowledge and no aptitude for actual battles; while Grant was a soldier to the marrow. This added to Grant's worries that he could at any time be bounced due to some political move. Halleck was but one of the thorns that would stick out and occasionally prick the sensitive Grant in addition to William Kountz and others who reverted to his drunkenness issue which was often a potent weapon against Grant.

Grant's next target was Fort Henry, an important fortification on the Tennessee River protecting a crucial piece of Confederate land. Grant superseded many of the admonitions of Halleck and other second-guessers and put in display another one of his trademarks - secrecy in carrying out his battle plans. Part of his plan was using the gun boat artillery from the ships commanded by Naval Officer Andrew Hull Foote. Showing personal involvement, decisiveness, and bravery, he pounced on Fort Henry and conquered it decisively. The victory gave enormous strategic advantages to the Union forces going forward.

In taking Fort Henry, he put on display his quickly developing traits as a commander: opportunistic, mobile, and scrappy. He also showed a benevolent and merciful side; even dining with captured Confederate officers and refraining from harshly punishing Confederate prisoners.

NINE: Dynamo

Next on Grant's agenda was another key Confederate
fortification in Tennessee, Fort Donelson. It was at a higher
elevation than Fort Henry and was considered a formidable
target. This time, Grant would apply one of his trademark
military gifts – a thorough knowledge of his opponent. In this
case, Grant knew how the mind of the Confederate generals
such as Gideon J. Pillow, John Floyd, and Simon Bolivar
Buckner worked. This was because he fought with the men in
previous battles and knew what strategies and tactics they
would employ. His gift (on rare deadly occasions a curse)
was that he could anticipate enemy reactions based on their
weaknesses and defects.

He did not fear or was fazed by the overgrown reputations of
Confederate generals as precise and invincible leaders because
he knew that they had weaknesses he could exploit. This type
of thinking made him appear to be confident and in-charge
of everything. Because of this, he was always offensive-
minded and despised those times when he had to make his
forces sit around and wait. This time, he executed an almost
perfect assault on Fort Donelson and, knowing that Pillow
and Floyd were not the aggressive types, conquered the

enemy decisively, forcing them into unconditional surrender as he took over the Fort's resources.

Aside from the unmatched respect he earned from his troops, he was venerated by the Confederate officers and soldiers that his forces caught as prisoners. He saw them as captured American citizens and treated them accordingly. Grant, when confronted personally with a corpse or a wounded man, cursed war and its terrible results. This feeling extended to his empathy for enemy combatants, captured or killed.

With very few other Union victories in other battlefields, Fort Donelson won him acclaim by the Northern press and pundits who christened him "Unconditional Surrender Grant," a play on his name, U.S. Grant. He also was promoted to Major General based on Halleck's recommendation. The win squarely put him in the White House limelight where President Lincoln, in approving his promotion, saw in Grant genuine and unique heroism and humility. It was the beginning of a special bond between the two men.

His success and acclaim however, did not impress his father-in-law Frederick Dent, who continued to be an unapologetic supporter of the Confederate cause. Not that it mattered to Grant now because he had found rousing success in his military calling. But with his success he would now forever be freed from Dent's influence and criticism.

But Grant was a restless maverick who never rested on his military victories. He swatted away personal issues and concentrated on following up on victories immediately, not allowing enemy forces to recuperate. He went on to take additional cities in Tennessee using his trademark aggressiveness.

His victories however started a disturbing pattern of many on his own side. Jealousy from Generals George McLellan and Halleck resurrected Grant's previous battles with alcoholism and used this against him even if an overwhelming majority of the charges were unfounded. He was severely disheartened by the charges and offered to resign even if he knew the charges were false. It was the sign of a truly reputable military leader – that he would follow whatever his superiors would do, and this included firing him.

In this instance, three people would emerge and rally to his defense. General William Tecumseh Sherman, a fellow West Pointer defended him as one who fought alongside him; his congressional sponsor Elihu Washburne also defended him by bending the ear of the one person whose opinion mattered most: Abraham Lincoln. This would be the start of a key alliance that would not only impact the fortunes of both men, but that of the country as well.

TEN: A Glittering Lie

After the decisive victories in Tennessee, the next step was to take Corinth further up the Tennessee River, which would pave the way for Vicksburg, Memphis, and broad swaths of the South. He was becoming frustrated with the incompetency of Halleck, who was politicizing the war to benefit those he favored. Despite his concerns about his commanders, he could not shed his aggressive nature in battle or lose focus in the face of battle.

In Shiloh, this aggressive stance resulted in a tunnel vision that was almost his downfall. Confident that the enemy did not also possess his attacking nature, he became complacent while waiting for other Union forces to organize around him. In Shiloh, in Western Tennessee he was caught by surprise by uncharacteristic aggression by two Confederate generals. His miscue cost seven thousand casualties in the initial attacks and was one of the very rare instances that he would abdicate responsibility for his actions by insisting that he was not caught unaware by the surprise assault on his forces.

In carrying out his duties however, he showed gallantry and bravery not otherwise exhibited by officers of his station. He rode horseback to the front of the battle lines, an inspiring maneuver that reinvigorated his troops. There was still a second day and he knew that the battle was not yet lost.

Reinforced by 25,000 troops from another company, Grant surprised the enemy by staging a pre-dawn attack that brought them on their heels. On this second day, Grant put into play what would be a trademark tactic – applying pressure on the enemy from as many places as he could. Eventually, the Confederate forces withdrew and Grant won the battle of attrition – over 24,000 wounded or killed putting the horrors or war in full focus. New technologies in ammunitions made killing easier and more brutal, and Grant was one of those who ironically shuddered at the terror that death and maiming brought.

In thy pyrrhic "victory" at Shiloh, there were ironically more Union casualties, but Grant showed his willingness to take titanic gambles while showing tremendous coolness under fire. Surviving the terrible depths of fortune of Shiloh was probably helped along by his enduring the ups and downs of his own personal life.

The empty victory did not escape the critical eyes of those back home. First, his initial setback was predictably blamed on unfounded claims of drunkenness fueled by Halleck and others; and second, his own military acumen and supposed brutality were called into question and prompted many to call for his removal and even, dismissal. Once again however, Elihu Washburne rushed to Grant's defense and Abraham Lincoln provided the final word on the issue and said that he "can't spare this man-he fights."

Through all the controversy Grant did not express any vehement disagreement with anything that the press or his detractors had. His only complaint was that he wanted his family kept out of the public argument about his alleged lapses.

Grant was at the time a guileless soldier with no political inclinations who failed to see the deceit around him, especially from double-dealers like Halleck. Instead of refuting the allegations, he offered to resign from the military. William Tecumseh Sherman, his closest military aid, talked him out of it, and Lincoln continued to throw his support behind Grant. It turned out that Grant didn't have to do much lobbying anyway.

In the second battle at Manassas (Bull Run) the Union forces under Halleck's protégé, George McLellan suffered a devastating defeat to the rebels. Lincoln quickly acted on the reversal and consolidated McLellan's forces under Grant. Lincoln had also lost his respect for Halleck after he began to

126

learn more about Halleck's hypocrisy and guile.

ELEVEN: Exodus

In Mississippi Grant continued to spar with Halleck, especially since Halleck wanted the army to show no mercy with the civilian population while Grant tended to be sympathetic towards everyone, especially innocent civilians. This compassionate dimension of Grant's personality complemented the Lincoln administration's developing policy of giving blacks more citizenship duties and rights. Grant issued a directive that runaway slaves should not be returned to their masters and be given employment within the army units if they chose to do so. In the overall scheme of things, the war aims of the North included the emancipation of slaves so the war had now reached a point of no return.

In 1862 Grant continued to score successes and by conquering the Northern Mississippi area, he was given command of a huge area by getting the commission of the Department of Tennessee. This was putting him on a collision course with the legendary head of the Confederate army, Robert Lee.

A big part of Grant's plan was to fully engage the use of Negroes whose potential as fighters he believed in. He received praise not only from his soldiers but from black leaders such as Frederick Douglass. Lincoln was supportive of Grant's aims to not only free the slaves, but to weaponize them and deploy them against their former masters.

In the meantime, other generals were not doing so well, which placed pressure on Lincoln and eventually Grant. George McLellan and Ambrose Burnside combined to incur big losses for the Potomac command. But in his usual coolness under fire Grant continued to master his Western area.

Grant found himself in the midst of the controversy around cotton trading, in which deceitful Southerners managed to sell their cotton to rapacious traders in the North. Unfortunately for Grant, he equated the crooked cotton trade almost exclusively to Jewish traders. In a rash move, he issued General Orders No. 11, where he prohibited Jews from any further trading. It was ironic that while he was emancipating blacks, he was outlawing Jews. Seeing the political prickliness of the decree, Lincoln immediately rescinded the order in what would be one of the very rare times that he would contradict Grant on any issue. Grant received widespread condemnation for his aborted and bigoted response, especially from the press.

In late 1862, after the union forces conquered New Orleans with the significant assistance of the Union navy under Dave Farragut, the path was open to take over Vicksburg, home of the only remaining Confederate fortress on the Mississippi river. Lincoln made a critical mistake by assigning John McClernand to oversee the Vicksburg assault. McClernand, a known opponent of Grant's, frittered away his opportunity to take Vicksburg, and Lincoln immediately rectified his error by placing Grant in command in the Mississippi campaign.

TWELVE: Man of Iron

Abraham Lincoln signed the Emancipation Proclamation on New Year's Day in 1863, officially ending slavery and turning the war into a winner-take-all proposition. Grant, who at the time did not have a political bone in his body, realized that the abolition of slavery, the root cause of the war, should be vigorously pursued, and he became an all-out proponent of Lincoln's policy, gearing his military efforts towards the pursuit of a tangible piece of policy.

The proclamation's biggest immediate impact on the war was to encourage the exodus of slaves from their Southern masters, which weakened the economic progress of the South while boosting the manpower levels of the Union forces.

In the meantime, Grant was suffering from debilitating bouts of migraine brought on by his worries about taking over Vicksburg. The headaches and his occasional need to be bedridden once again brought on rumors of alcohol problems which he refuted and which Julia Grant, hundreds of miles away, denounced.

Vicksburg presented a host of problems the most pressing of which was the occasional flooding brought on by the overflow of the Mississippi River. Grant never stopped thinking of ways to overcome obstacles, and this extended to resorting to non-military solutions including engineering ones. While these initiatives showed that he was not afraid to innovate and take chances, they also led to expensive failures that deterred to advance his military goals. The failures stoked impatience in the North and some even thought Grant to be an imbecile. Of course, the inevitable charges of drunkenness were levelled against him, most if not all of which were untrue.

Even while Lincoln continued to throw his support behind Grant, Secretary of War Edwin Stanton was not too sure. He sent his undersecretary Charles Dana, undercover of analyzing war pay, to spy on Grant to determine if the stories about his drinking were true. Dana expected to find an inebriated and disorganized Grant, but instead found a sober, likeable, and extremely focused commander. Over time, Dana revealed what his real objectives were and ended up being one of Grant's closest friends.

As Vicksburg continued to consume him, Grant decided that nothing less than a direct, frontal attack on the rebel fortification was needed. He devised an attack comprised of naval bombardment to draw fire from the rebels after which he would march his troops along the Mississippi river's west bank, combining surprise and a massive force of men. He would also use Sherman to divert attention from another side of the Vicksburg fortification while his main force launched their decisive attack.

It all worked. What impressed observers more than his military strategy was his unruffled nature in the midst of overseeing a plan comprised of many complicated and interlocking parts, deploying tens of thousands of men and uncountable pieces of artillery and military craft.

By the morning of May 17, 1863, Grant's forces were within ten miles of Vicksburg and all it took was to employ brute force in sending up a huge force through the swamps, marshes and trees surrounding Vicksburg. The tally at the end of the Vicksburg incursion was a rout. Grant had 276 casualties to the rebels' 1,751. As his forces marched through the conquered town, former slaves cheered him on while independent observers could only marvel at the stunning success commandeered by a man who displayed uncommon equanimity and focus in a difficult and complicated situation.

THIRTEEN: Citadel

In another trademark move, Grant would follow-up his conquest immediately by attacking the backtracking rebel forces in Vicksburg. His plan would have worked except that on May 22 John McClernand provided exaggerated information about his troops' conquests of rebel strongholds. An incensed Grant momentarily lost his façade of placid countenance when he realized that McClernand's duplicity had just cost him the lives of thousands of Union soldiers and valuable time. It also bothered Grant immensely that there were thousands of Union corpses that he could not properly provide proper identification and disposal.

Having lost the element of surprise, Grant resorted to a classic siege maneuver in which he decided that he would just choke off supply of rations and munitions from the surrounded city. He hated siege arrangements like this because he detested sitting down and waiting for things to unfold. He wanted to take action on the battlefield instead of letting nature take its course. The sitting around and waiting took a toll on Grant's otherwise impeccable calm and quiet strength. Despite the presence of his young son Fred in the Vicksburg campaign, he sometimes looked troubled and disheveled, which, for the umpteenth time brought on suspicions of drinking. The truth about Grant's drinking was that he was not a habitual drinker – the big problem is that he could not drink moderately and alcohol quickly affected his senses and his physical appearance and actions.

Whether drunk or not, Grant continued to bombard Vicksburg and kept it closed from the outside world. The Confederate Commander in Vicksburg, John C. Pemberton, had pinned his hopes that another Confederate general, Joe Johnston, would swoop in and help redeem his troops. Unfortunately for the rebels, Grant's formations prevented any such attempt to provide reinforcements for the Confederate army under siege.

In the meantime, Grant increased the numbers of his forces by taking in runaway slaves that he would utilize in future campaigns. While generally successful, the program met with some resistance even from Northerners who continued to think that Negroes were an inferior race. The converted slaves however, acquitted themselves well in battle, especially in Milliken's Bend on June 7, 1863, when mostly black troops overran a rebel stronghold even while supplied with inferior equipment. The defeat was a shock to Southern sensibilities who believed that Negroes were only good for slave labor.

The siege had reduced Pemberton's forces into a scared, hungry, and demoralized contingent. After hearing of a proposed assault by Grant slated for July 4, 1863, Pemberton decided to wave the white flag of surrender. As he did with other surrendering forces, Grant treated Pemberton's surrendering army with compassion and fairness.

FOURTEEN: Deliverance

Vicksburg provided stark evidence of a few truths. First, Grant was a benevolent conqueror who considered his captives U.S. citizens who would one day be productive members of society again, so there was no need to stomp on them and gloat about their losses. Second, there was a huge disparity between the well-being and robustness of the rebels and the Union soldiers, who enjoyed better provisions and facilities.

Even in the face of impertinence by captured commanders such as Pemberton, Grant impressed the civilians in the captured towns with his egalitarian and humble nature. The adulation that he received, however, was muted. If he had been an eastern commander, he would have no doubt received much more acclaim, but not that he cared.

The important thing for Grant was winning battles and moving the Union forces closer to victory. His triumph in Vicksburg was a devastating loss for the rebels that seemed to be the beginning of the end for the Confederate rebellion. When Lincoln got the formal notice of Vicksburg's capitulation, his respect for Grant grew even bigger. At this juncture, Lincoln accorded Grant the biggest evidence of presidential admiration – direct communication and contact with President Lincoln himself.

His victory at Vicksburg dispelled all doubt about his drinking and any doubt about his abilities as a military leader. As a result, Lincoln approved Grant's promotion to Major General on July 7, 1863, just days after his Vicksburg triumph, giving him two stars and placing him one step closer to Lieutenant General. More than rank, it gave Grant a big measure of economic security with the corresponding increase in pay. While there was talk of giving Grant generalship over the Potomac or eastern forces, he quickly quashed the notion and refused to pursue it, showing his disdain for any political maneuvering.

When Rawlins delivered the final official report on the Vicksburg triumph to Lincoln and his Cabinet, the president was, more than ever, a gushing fan of Grant and his exploits, saying that Grant moves things wherever he is. More impressive was the continued display by Grant of his kindness to civilians in conquered areas. Eschewing William Tecumseh Sherman's marauding forays, where his forces stripped captured cities of their provisions and productive equipment, Grant urged his men to take only what was necessary for their immediate needs and leave the rest to the citizens of the cities. Going one step further, he distributed medicine and provisions to the needy people in those cities.

As military recruitment efforts in the east soured the importance of incorporating former slaves into the Union, force was magnified. Grant continued to urge his commanders to supply and train Negroes to be members of their fighting forces, a move that ingratiated himself and Lincoln to an ever-grateful black population.

There was a relatively long lull in fighting, which, while allowing Grant to revel in the adulation offered by his growing legion of admirers, also led him to be careless. Once again, a few occasional drinking sessions to which he allowed himself were blown up to be fits of drunkenness. When he fell off his horse and seriously injured himself in August 1863, the rumors started swirling anew, although these would do little to sour his career unlike with previous incidents. Instead, Grant was handpicked by Lincoln to spearhead a brand-new Military Division of the Mississippi that widened his command in the western territories.

In this new role, he headed to the frontlines in Tennessee for more military adventure.

FIFTEEN: Above the Clouds

In October 1863 Grant headed off to the Tennessee border near Georgia to continue to put pressure on the Confederate's western strongholds. Here, he gained another key supporter in Captain Horace Porter, who found Grant's well-prepared and organized mind, and the volume of knowledge of complicated logistical facts complemented his firm grasp of military strategy. This was a tribute to Grant because Porter placed third in class at West Point and was no intellectual slouch.

In surveying the Union forces in the area, Grant concluded that the first order of the day was to restore Union troops' morale and health by opening new routes to bring supplies through key rail junctures. The provisions he provided once again magnified the wide gulf between the sustenance and health of Confederate and Union soldiers, the latter becoming, on average, more robust and healthy.

He decided that the key in winning the western war was taking over Chattanooga. He saw that the Confederate forces were well-entrenched and seemed to possess an advantage in morale after whipping the forces of Union Generals

Ambrose Burnside, William S. Rosecrans, and George Thomas. Grant felt that his superior numbers and knowledge of the opposing generals was enough advantage to overrun the well-fortified city.

His approach was to use an overwhelming force of 80,000 men to encircle the Confederate forces and attack it from different sides. Beginning on November 24, he had three generals – Sherman, Thomas, and Joe Hooker – assault the Confederate forces from different areas to execute his plan. While the landscape towards the enemy lines was littered with all sorts of natural impediments, Grant was heartened to see his generals and soldiers display uncommon valor and persistence to break through the natural barriers and overcome the enemy forces.

The Union forces finally took over Chattanooga with thousands less casualties than the rebels. After two failed attempts by other Union generals in previous battles in Tennessee, Grant showed the world that he was a cut above the other generals of his era. His fame reached even higher levels by integrating three disparate elements of the Union army. He also displayed sheer personal bravery by riding his horse into battle, and was quickly becoming a legendary figure. That Lincoln personally congratulated Grant for his efforts was testimony to his burgeoning reputation.

Grant's soaring popularity generated the eventual whispers that he was interested in running for President in the elections coming up in 1864. This made Lincoln a little wary of the Grant mystique, which made him a little less sanguine about elevating Grant to even higher pedestals as the rest of the country wanted Lincoln to do. A bill came up in Congress recommending that Grant be given his third star as a Lieutenant General, which Lincoln set aside temporarily.

All Lincoln's qualms were put to rest when Grant announced that he had no political ambitions and that his only goal was to turn back the rebel Confederacy. The two men would continue to share common vision for the country, and were committed to the principle that all men, including blacks, had a God-given right to share in the United States' democratic processes.

SIXTEEN: Idol of the Hour

With his unassailable stature coupled with his huge military successes, the bill to have Grant elevated to a three-star general seemed like a given. Ironically, one of the most hesitant persons about the promotion was Grant himself who wondered if being promoted to Lieutenant General would pin him to a desk job. The tide, however, was too strong, and Grant's promotion came through with the additional perk of being personally awarded his new rank by President Lincoln in Washington D.C. It would be the first time that both men would set eyes on each other after years of communicating by telegram.

Typical of Grant was his loyalty to those close to him and personal success was something that he wanted to share. He lobbied for Rawlins to get a commission as Brigadier General in repayment of Rawlins' tireless service not only in military matters, but in being Grant's watchdog against his drunkenness.

He also brought his son Fred with him to Washington D.C. in March 1864, when his small stature and his simple and unadorned manner rendered him inconspicuous wherever he went until he was announced as the famed U.S. Grant -

whereupon pandemonium usually broke loose.

In their very first meeting, Abraham Lincoln beheld the much smaller (by eight inches) man as quiet and taciturn, but greeted him with much enthusiasm, recognizing Grant's value to his administration and to the nation. Grant received a rousing response from Lincoln's Cabinet soon after, after Lincoln himself gave a glowing introduction to the country's newest Lieutenant General. Grant had a disarming personality, and his warm, personal manner was not overflowing with charm, but neither did he ruffle any feathers or seem threatening even with his growing powers and influence.

It was time for Lincoln and Grant to discuss giving Grant dominion over the entire military operation of the Union forces. In their private conversation, Lincoln stressed his support for Grant and told his general that he would leave all military decisions to Grant while he supplied Grant's armies with whatever support they needed, providing whatever it took to defeat the rebel armies. Lincoln was a big advocate of Grant's style of quick and decisive action, especially since the war was costing the government millions every day, leading to a serious budget deficit.

After returning to Nashville, Grant reshuffled his military

brain trust, placing his close friend William Tecumseh Sherman over Halleck, who, as it turned out, appreciated being relegated to what was essentially a desk job; one that he felt he was more suited for. He also met with his generals to discuss his general strategy of applying maximum pressure to Robert F. Lee who led the Confederate Army's western forces, and Joseph Johnston, who was running their eastern operation.

Even as Grant and Julia began to enjoy the accolades and perks associated with Grant's new lofty commission, defeating Lee and the Confederate Army was his utmost prerogative. He was more than ever, itching for a fight

SEVENTEEN: Ulysses the Silent

As the war progressed, it became very clear that the Union army's advantage in numbers would continue to increase as the South was having a hard time recruiting new soldiers even after they relaxed the age requirements. By the spring of 1864, the rebel forces would have shrunk to a much smaller force, and the Union army was poised to apply a grand and unified strategy under its new Lieutenant General.

Grant combined the western and eastern armies into a single cohesive force, where the battles fought by one unit would be part of an overall offensive strategy that complemented the other units. He would use both armies to overcome the two major forces of the rebels – Johnston's in Georgia and more importantly Lee's in Virginia. Grant would apply unrelenting pressure on the Confederate side, using his advantage in numbers, material, and organization.

In shaping the team to carry out his strategy, he restored professional soldiers from the North such as George McLellan and John Fremont to help rally the North behind the war effort. He shed political generals such as Benjamin Butler and Nathaniel Banks. He also made sure he kept

Rawlins to function both as a military and spiritual advisor, making sure Grant did not recede back to alcoholism when things got tough. He then recruited his close friend Ely Parker, a native American Indian to be his staff secretary.

To maximize his fighting forces, he uprooted scores of army personnel from their desk jobs and trained and equipped them to be at the ready for deployment to the standing army. He continued to encourage the recruitment of black soldiers to improve his already overwhelming edge in numbers. Finally, Grant would end up posting himself near Virginia, which revealed his immediate and overriding concern – to smash Robert Lee's forces in the state.

He would take personal action for this showdown with Lee, a battle that was fraught with many risks and with much downside. But he would be quick when he had to act on his own judgements and accepted responsibility readily for the results, good or bad. As a general, he did not excite anyone with bluster and was as simple a man as a general would ever be. He moved among his troops as if he were one of them and exuded an air of quiet authority. This went a long way in shoring up the morale of the Army of the Potomac in the East that lost many a battle when Grant was not at the helm of those forces.

The most important person in Grant's orbit, however, on any side of the conflict was Robert Lee, at the time the most outstanding graduate that West Point had ever produced. Lee seemed to possess almost supernatural powers as he won battle after battle against armies in the eastern theater.

But while Lee was the master of individual skirmishes, Grant lorded over everyone in crafting master strategy. In the summer of 1863, however, Lee would have a big advantage as he had already successfully defended Virginia against other Union generals, and he proved almost invincible in the state. Lee's dwindling manpower and resources, however, meant that he had to be on the defensive and could ill-afford to gamble on offensive maneuvers.

As fall set in, the stage was set for the ultimate showdown between the master generals of the Civil War as the fate of their respective sides hung in the balance.

EIGHTEEN: Raging Storm

On April 30 1864, probably sensing that the war was approaching its apex with the pending confrontation between Grant and Lee, President Lincoln sent a note to Grant reiterating his support for the troops and that he was extremely satisfied with how Grant had conducted the war to date. The climax of the Civil War was coming and Lincoln's unsolicited letter seemed to only magnify the scale and importance of things to come.

The big order for Grant for this battle was how to move a gargantuan mass of 115,000 men through the Rapidan River and the surrounding areas of Richmond without tipping Lee of his moves. On May 4, Grant, with his ardent sponsor Congressman Washburne observing, moved towards the Rapidan in what he thought would be a quick and effortless gallop into Richmond. Instead, Grant's offensive turned into the bloody seven-week Overland campaign which resulted in almost 90,000 casualties including over 7,000 Union Army deaths.

With a combination of dense foliage and well-fortified rebel encampment, Grant's forces were embroiled in an agonizing advance that resulted in human attrition rarely seen in conflict. Just after two days and thousands of Union deaths, Grant slid back into his tent and uncharacteristically sunk into a depressed stupor, agitated to no end for sending so many men to their deaths.

In true Grant fashion, however, he quickly bounced back and wrote Lincoln to tell him that he would pursue this segment of the war to its just conclusion. For Grant suffering the horrible losses was part of his overall scheme of continually battering Lee's forces and eventually knocking him down into submission with his overwhelming advantage in manpower. History would record the Overland campaign as a "strategic win" for Grant's forces even if they suffered significantly more casualties. Within this battle, Grant lost many mini-battles, but each one meant incremental manpower losses for Lee that he could not replace, while Grant had a seemingly endless supply of bodies to replenish the men he lost.

This was the acknowledged sentiment in the rebel camp. They knew very well what Grant was up to but there was nothing much they could do about it. They would be in a defensive position for the rest of the war.

NINETEEN: Heavens Hung in Black

Throughout the rest of May 1864, errors and miscommunications by some of Grant's generals led to the delay of Grant's advance and eroded the confidence of the Northern citizens who were eager for good news. Instead, they were informed of many deaths which gave an impression that the Confederate army was somehow gaining an edge. Grant's overall military strategy mattered less to the population who measured success or failure by the number of soldiers that came back as corpses or were never heard from again.

After a month of the Overland campaign, Grant saw the weariness in his men's faces, but Grant's plan of attrition was just continuing to take shape. His incursions were slow but steady, and even as he lost men at a frightful rate, his forces gained territory that continued to shrink Lee's world. Grant's forces also tore up railroads and jammed up supply routes to further choke up Lee's sources of reinforcements and supplies.

The public of course did not see these subtle gains as wins, and Grant needed a resounding battle win. On June 3 Grant sent 60,000 men straight towards Confederate embankments in Cold Harbor in what was supposed to be a massive show of force. In this battle, Grant's numbers proved no equal to the natural barriers that the wilderness provided, and the well-entrenched rebels. In less than two hours, the Union army suffered over 7,000 casualties to only 1,500 for the rebels.

The press and critics called Grant a "butcher" for sending men and boys to their sure deaths. But while the citizens and Grant's critics gnashed their teeth at the staggering loss of lives, the "lost battle" resulted in Lee's forces being forced to move eighty miles further South, which robbed him of any mobility for any offensive action.

President Lincoln, even with the knowledge that his re-election chances hinged on the success or failure of Grant in his standoff with Lee, continued to convey to Grant his reassurance that the army still had his support and welcomed whatever efforts that Grant was planning.

With the mounting casualties however, Grant was prepared to temporarily spurn his offensive mentality and capitalize on the unfolding elements of situation. Rather than embarking on continual series of attacks that would lead to many more casualties, he decided to sit back and wait. With Lee's army stuck in their fortifications without any chance for offensive action, Grant decided on inaction rather than action – he would defeat Lee by siege, essentially starving the Confederate forces into submission.

TWENTY: Caldron of Hell

In late June of 1864, Grant accelerated his plans for the siege on Lee's forces. All of the roads leading up to Richmond were destroyed to prevent Lee's forces from getting resupplied. Sensing Grant's plans to box him in, Lee sent one of his few remaining forces outside Richmond under Jubal Early, to attack the cities in the Northeast to hopefully force Grant to divert some of his forces from the Richmond area. Lincoln, in what was probably his only "order", however thinly veiled, suggested that Grant remove troops from his siege maneuver in Petersburg and send them to Washington to defend against the rebels.

Instead of moving troops from his siege of Richmond, Grant suggested that the North recruit three hundred thousand men and add them to the existing forces. Grant sent a young and aggressive general Philip Sheridan to defeat Early and take command of the Shenandoah Valley, successfully defending the Northeast. To make matters worse for the Confederate forces, on August 5, 1864 Admiral Farragut of the Union Navy punched through rebel forces in Mobile Bay in Alabama, effectively sealing off one of the last major Southern ports that would have allowed supplies to stream in to help Lee's beleaguered forces.

Through most of the summer of 1863, Grant hatched many plans that ended in disaster, including his plan to build booby-trapped tunnels leading to Lee's encampment. Because of the unevenness and unpredictability of the terrain, the mines that they planted exploded prematurely, causing several deaths from a terrifying blaze that they named the "Caldron of Fire." The explosions created a huge crater that became a symbol to some critics of Grant's ineptness. Once again, charges of alcoholism that came up somehow explained fiascos like the crater. His siege would go on for nine months and Grant treated sitting around as his new attack mode, essentially waiting for Lee's forces to wither and die.

Through Grant's ups and downs, John Rawlins was the steadying force in his life, protecting him from alcohol temptations but mostly just being a steadying influence in a gut-wrenching war. Rawlins however, began to suffer the first stages of tuberculosis and appeared to be severely weakened, alarming Grant on occasion.

Unbeknownst to Grant's critics, his war of attrition had placed a tenacious choke hold on Lee's defensive position in Richmond. The Southern populace saw in Grant a man who would not give in despite setbacks

unlike other Union generals before him, and they were preparing for the eventual capitulation to the Union side.

TWENTY-ONE: Chew & Choke

As the summer of 1864 set in, Grant would continue to pound Lee's defenses, probing the weaknesses that he knew he would eventually find. Lincoln was thrilled about Grant's relentlessness and exhorted Grant to "chew and choke" with a bulldog grip as much as possible.

But the nation did not share Lincoln's enthusiasm for Grant's handling of the war. The appalling casualty levels without any seeming end in sight were beginning to jeopardize not only Lincoln's chances of reelection but the electoral fate of the Republican Party as well. Some members of Congress created new factions to distance themselves from Lincoln and the war thinking that associating themselves with Lincoln and Grant was political poison. But even if Grant seemed to flounder in his siege of Lee's forces, many still considered him to be viable replacement for Lincoln, who was increasingly being seen as inept and unforceful.

Like everyone else, Lincoln had no inkling of Grant's political aspirations or even if he supported the president and his party at all. Lincoln sent an envoy to get Grant's categorical statement on where Grant stood politically. Grant emphatically replied that he was throwing his full support behind Lincoln and the war effort, and had zero aspirations for political office. This private exchange between Lincoln and Grant emboldened both men to continue with their push to oust Lee and bring the rebels to their knees.

As the presidential elections neared, the Republican National Committee decided that Lincoln had no chance to win reelection with the way the war was going and asked him to try to negotiate a settlement with Jefferson Davis without having them renounce slavery, and water down his emancipation program.

On their end, the Democrats nominated George McLellan as their candidate for president on August 31 1864, on a platform of cessation of the current hostilities and the negotiation of a peace settlement with the South, suggesting that the Union's wartime goals were ultimately futile. But Grant and his forces had a surprise in store.

Just two days later, Sherman triumphantly reported to Grant that they had overrun Atlanta together with its crucial railway hub. When the news was broadcast in Washington, the factions calling for a peace settlement disbanded and the Democratic Party quickly shed its "peace plank" from its official campaign platform.

While Grant's and Sheridan's personal bonds were strengthening, Sheridan kept on pounding Confederate forces and decisively eradicated the only rebel company left outside of Lee's entrenched position in Petersburg and Richmond. Sherman had already decimated Atlanta, and by December 20, had "liberated" the city, in effect reducing the Confederacy to a mere shell.

Despite the toll in human lives and expense, Grant's military strategy had worked. The goal of breaking apart Confederate forces was a rousing success with just some minor details left to complete the Union victory.

TWENTY-TWO: Her Satanic Majesty

In December 1864, with the Shenandoah Valley all sewed up, Sheridan was able to move his troops to Petersburg to further swell up Grant's forces in what Grant felt would be the final stage of his siege of Lee's army. The outcome was so academic that Julia Grant was allowed a visit to Grant in January 1865 as hostilities began to die down.

Lee was down to 57,000 men compared to Grant's 124,000 after Sheridan's forces transferred to Grant's main army. A desperate Jefferson Davis, trying to avoid what he knew would be Grant's call for unconditional surrender sent a negotiating team made up of his Vice-President Alexander Stephens, his Senate President and Secretary of War on January 29, 1865. When things went on a standstill, Grant, using the political capital he had amassed with Lincoln, convinced the president to meet the Southern commissioners himself to try to work something out.

By the time that Lincoln arrived for his meeting with the commissioners on February 3, however, the U.S. Congress had passed Lincoln's Thirteenth Amendment, which outlawed slavery. Armed with this legislative win, Lincoln gave the commissioners his three conditions for surrender: One, an end to slavery; two, his armies would not stop hostilities until all the Confederate forces were abandoned; and three, that the Union would be permanently restored. The commissioners were taken aback by Lincoln's unbending terms and slunk back to Davis to deliver the news that there could be no negotiation.

In the meantime, Grant did Lincoln a huge personal favor by accommodating his son Robert to be part of his army retinue over the objections of Lincoln's wife Mary, who was losing her tenuous hold on sanity after having lost two young boys and then having to agree to have her eldest enter the fray of battle just as things were winding down. Her fragile mental state extended to the crass treatment to a point in which she extended Julia Grant during their time together in Virginia and even through what would turn out to be Lincoln's final days.

In the meantime, Lee was dealing with many desertions while trying to keep whatever was left of his army fed and inspired. Some in the South even suggested what was considered abhorrent to that point: recruit Negroes for their army to compensate for the dwindling number of combatants. While they were mulling their options, Sherman was doing cleanup work in taking over North and South Carolina, choking off the final points of supply for the South.

Lee's last gasp was to try to take over Fort Stedman, one of the Grant strongholds in Petersburg. When he failed to maintain his advantage and relinquished Fort Stedman, he knew in his heart that everything was lost.

TWENTY-THREE: Dirty Boots

After Lincoln's departure, Grant was itching to put the finishing touches on his victory over Robert Lee. He agreed with an antsy Sheridan that they should not let up at the current stage and provide the North the victory that it deserved. Grant, becoming more astute politically, also wanted to give a Northern general some acclaim so that the entire country could share in the victory laurels. Besides, the war was costing the country $4 million a day and could probably not bear much more.

On March 29, 1865, Sheridan started the final assault on Lee's forces in Virginia. This was something that the Confederate States' president foresaw, and he pondered leaving his home in Richmond the night prior to the first assault. On April 1, 1865, the fight was all over as Sheridan totally stamped out the last rebel stronghold. Grant subsequently captured the rebel strongholds in Petersburg, and he relayed news of his victory to Lincoln who spread the news to an exultant Northern populace eager to put an end to hostilities.

All that was left was to weaken Lee's forces totally by cutting them off from their supply sources, and on April 4 Sheridan's forces set off to try to cut off Lee's army from any source of sustaining his troops. By April 5, the rebels dropped from exhaustion, starvation, and hunger, and Lee knew that there was no point in further resistance if they could not get re-supplied.

On April 7 Grant sent Lee a letter requesting him to surrender. After receiving the letter that night, Lee crafted a response asking for the terms of surrender that Grant wanted. On April 8, Grant responded that nothing less than an unconditional surrender was acceptable, which meant that they were not allowed to take up arms against the U.S. again. Lee, however would still stand his ground and hope that he could get re-supplied.

But when Lee learned that his supply sources had been cut off by Sheridan, he had no options left. He sent Grant a letter that stated that he would be willing to meet and sign for whatever surrender terms that Grant needed, and they scheduled a meeting at court house in Appomattox on April 9.

When they finally met, Grant was in awe with the venerable Lee, who was fifteen years older, and under whom he served under during the Mexican War. Grant tried to exchange pleasantries which were politely rebuffed by Lee who understandably was tied up in knots as he was giving up the fight for millions of Southerners who had passionately supported the rebel cause for four years.

Despite the violence between the armies of both men, Grant was extraordinarily generous with his post-surrender actions. He allowed Lee to keep his sword and promised adequate provisions and transport for the 25,000 men left under Lee's command in Virginia. Grant also allowed them to keep their sidearms and refused to decree extremely punitive measures against not only the soldiers but the populace. Grant's compassion at Appomattox would be an icon for post-war benevolence for the ages.

For the vanquished, however, the most difficult provision for Southerners to accept was the planned granting of full citizenship rights to Negroes. Most Southerners believed in all their heart that Negroes were beneath whites in terms of intelligence and skill, a concept that was thoroughly thrashed with how the Negroes acquitted themselves in Grant's military during the war.

In announcing Lee's surrender, Lincoln triumphantly made what would turn out to be his final speech in front of thousands of deliriously happy Northern citizens. One of the few unhappy exceptions in the audience was his future murderer John Wilkes Booth, who simmered at the notion of Negroes being considered the equal of whites.

The war would be but a chapter in Grant's storied life. A failure in his civilian life, he was a rousing success as a military leader who was also just beginning to mature as an astute politician; and as he matured, so did the country. As the Civil War began, many European observers believed that the nation would not be able to withstand the war which left 750,000 dead and millions more in dire poverty.

It was time for the next chapter for Grant, and together with a new United States of America, they were going to prove the naysayers wrong.

TWENTY-FOUR: A Singular, Indescribable Vessel

When Ulysses and Julia Grant arrived in Washington D.C., they were greeted by huge crowds that spilled into the streets to catch a glimpse of the American hero. Once again, Mary Lincoln gave the cold shoulder to Julia Grant, sensing that Ulysses might be a rival to her husband.

When Grant was ushered into the Cabinet meeting on the morning of April 14, 1865, he was met with enthusiastic applause. Aside from regaling the Cabinet with his war stories, he reiterated his commitment to the terms with Robert Lee at Appomattox that the Southerners would be allowed to their homes unmolested and get on with their lives.

After the meeting, Grant and Lincoln were warned that there were many suspicious elements around town that combined with whispers about assassination attempts on their lives. Political fires were very much inflamed, but Lincoln had dismissed these fears as an unavoidable part of their jobs and eschewed any special protection. All throughout the day, the Grants felt that they were being closely watched and observed. On a carriage ride, a stranger on horseback actually peered into their cab. They found out a few days later that the stranger was John Wilkes Booth.

Lincoln invited the Grants to join them to watch a comedy play that night at Ford's Theater not only to give the Grants some recreational time but to allow Lincoln to present Ulysses Grant to what was sure to be an adoring theater crowd. Turning down Lincoln's invitation may have saved his and Julia's life. At 10:13 that night Booth bounded into Ford's theater and shot Lincoln point blank. Lincoln would die just a few hours later not even seeing the dawn.

Grant was thrust into work immediately as Stanton asked him to see to the defense and security of Washington, which was thrust into paranoia with the Civil War just having ended. Grant's promise of compassion towards the vanquished South was seriously tested as he seemed to go on the warpath again, this time to assiduously search for his close friend's assassins and plotters. Even as he had no political office, Grant was pressed into an unwanted role as the caretaker of a wounded nation, enlisted not necessarily to fight an enemy but to heal a nation hurting from war and the loss of its beloved leader.

The cruel joke that fate played on the nation did not end with the assassination of Lincoln but with the elevation of his vice-president Andrew Johnson to take his place.

As it turns out Johnson was merely playing lip service to the grand plans that Lincoln had about emancipation and equality of all races. After assuming the presidency, he not only showed that his populism was directed on poor white people. It did not include the Negroes that Lincoln had worked so hard to emancipate. His true colors surfaced as he began to argue against the evils of the Abolition and Negroes' lack of qualifications to be granted full citizenship rights.

Grant, who at first tried hard to be decorous towards his new president, found it increasingly difficult to side with the man who slowly drifted to the side of the Southern racism that had started the war in the first place. He also had to defend his good friend William T. Sherman from lies that Johnson was spreading to tarnish the soldier's reputation. When Sherman was accorded his final military glory for conquering the very last vestige of Southern rebellion, Grant was sure to attend the parade for his best friend, the peak of their friendship which would soon be tested as Grant would take on life's newest challenge: Politics.

PART THREE: A LIFE OF PEACE

TWENTY-FIVE: Soldierly Good Faith

As leader of the U.S. Armed Forces, Grant reduced the country's standing army from 1 million to 210,000 soldiers intent on making it not the biggest army in the world but the best. In a portent of (sometimes bad) things to come, he staffed his military hierarchy with those closest to him, including Robert Lincoln, Ely Parker, and his brother-in-law Fred Dent. And despite his differences with his father-in-law Grant, allowed him to stay with him in Washington.

Being the head of the Armed Forces also meant that he and his family had to live in Washington, where the rich and powerful lived and worked. He certainly had very rich friends who provided him with houses not only to live in, but to vacation in. One of these was Abel Corbin who would marry Grant's sister Jennie, and figure in a financial scandal in Grant's imminent and inevitable political future. While Grant continued to live a normal life even with his lofty position (he took the cable car to work every day), Julia perked up in the heady atmosphere of Washington politics and society. While Grant shunned public appearances and functions, Julia basked in their glitz and pomp.

Despite his differences with Johnson, Grant initially maintained an amicable relationship with the unpredictable president. Soon however, he found himself not only questioning Johnson's views but eventually clashing with him on crucial issues, especially those related to Negro suffrage and with the way Johnson publicly denigrated black people, saying that America was a country for white men.

Johnson's version of "Reconstruction" meant providing citizenship to Southerners if they took an oath of allegiance. The second part was to hold elections to create a governing hierarchy in the Southern states with the startling provision that blacks could not vote in the elections. Worse, Johnson announced that, as president, he reserved the right to override any agreements that were entered in in Appomattox, a treaty that Grant completely invested himself in. Johnson seemed to suggest that Grant exceeded his treaty-making authority when he dealt with Robert Lee, who Johnson maintained should be immediately arrested.

After learning about Johnson's view of his peace treaty, he gave reassurances to Lee that their agreement would be honored by the U.S. government. On July 16, 1985, he had a testy meeting with Johnson, in which he reiterated that it would be a big mistake to vacate the terms of the Appomattox treaty. After the meeting, Johnson softened his rhetoric and desisted from arresting Lee.

In a sign that Grant's political instincts still needed some honing, he wanted to put the finishing touches on the Civil War by making his intentions known that he wanted to prop up the Mexican government to repulse a drive by Ferdinand Maximilian to overthrow the Mexican government. He had an unnecessary fight with Seward on whether Grant still had jurisdiction over the conflict, especially since the war was officially over. He believed that the forces of Maximilian provided a refuge for Confederate soldiers. He was bailed out when Mexico took matters into their own hands and executed Ferdinand.

Grant's back and forth with Johnson about what to do about Negroes in the South continued unabated as they received conflicting reports about the situation of blacks and the Reconstruction. In the process, he was getting sometimes painful lessons in politics when his words would sometimes be twisted and taken against him. In the overall picture, he was improving his chops as a politician, but, more importantly, he was not abandoning the spirit of promoting freedom and racial equality.

TWENTY-SIX: Swing around the Circle

While Grant was living up to the promises of abolition and the terms of the Appomattox surrender agreement, Andrew Johnson seemed hell bent on reversing them. When he voted not to extend a Lincoln pet project the Freedmen's Bureau, it signaled that he had no interest in protecting freed slaves' welfare. The Bureau had been established to provide assistance to former slaves, including fuel, food, clothing, and temporary shelter. In March 1866, he also vetoed a bill to nullify racist Black Codes in the South that prevented blacks from owning property and freely engaging in commerce. He then publicly stated that white immigrants had a better claim to citizenship because they had a better understanding of how democratic institutions worked in America. Finally, Johnson vetoed (which was overridden) the Fourteenth Amendment, which gave each citizen (including blacks') equal rights before the law.

In a departure from Johnson's rhetoric and actions, Grant continued to use his troops to protect blacks in the South who were increasingly being persecuted. In the notorious Mechanics convention riots in New Orleans, Grant threw his considerable protective influence to shield black people from

174

violence after many blacks were murdered. When Johnson seemed to say that the murders were based on overblown stories, Grant began to find Johnson's policies increasingly intolerable. Grant also disarmed southern armories to ensure that Southern whites who were against abolition did not get their hands on weaponry.

Looking forward to the elections in 1868 Johnson tried to make it appear that Grant, whose political interests were unknown, was on his side by making sure that Grant was present during his public appearances. Grant also swatted away any questions about his plans to run for office especially going up against Johnson for the Republican nomination, which made Johnson's ruse more effective.

But in a public and personal rebuke of Johnson, Grant refused to go to Mexico to intercede in a dispute between the Mexican government and rebels. Despite keeping his political intentions private, Johnson knew that after this incident, Grant was squarely in opposition against him. As he continued to contest and contravene the terms of the Appomattox surrender and the government's abolitionist philosophy, the calls for Johnson's impeachment began to grow. It did not help Johnson that in the 1866 elections Radical Republicans won a big chunk of seats in Congress ensuring that the opposition against Johnson would only continue to grow.

In March 1867, the House passed the first Reconstruction Act, which called for the continued assistance of ex-slaves and the granting of more citizenship rights for them. Johnson vetoed the bill but was easily overridden. Congress also passed the Tenure of Office Act meant to protect Lincoln Cabinet appointees. Under the new act, removing a Cabinet member required a congressional vote instead of allowing a president to unilaterally remove the Cabinet member. This was passed to protect Lincoln's Secretary of War Stanton, who Johnson had threatened to dismiss.

Johnson also opposed a second Reconstruction Act that called for federal troops to intervene in behalf of ex-slaves who were being persecuted. This became even more imperative when the Ku Klux Klan, founded in mid-1866 by Confederate veterans, increased the level of their murderous violence over blacks. On July 18, 1867, Grant finally testified before a House Judiciary Committee that was contemplating filing articles of impeachment against Johnson. Grant testified that he was intent on following the spirit of the surrender terms he made with Robert Lee while Johnson appeared to be trying to supersede them.

A day later, Congress passed a third Reconstruction Act which gave military district commanders wide latitude in enforcing voting rights.

It was now left for the Radical Republicans to try to convince Grant to contest Johnson for the Republican nomination for the upcoming elections coming in 1868. While they didn't know if he would consent to their recruitment, they knew that he was squarely against the rogue sitting president.

TWENTY-SEVEN: Volcanic Passion

While Grant and Henry Stanton sometimes did not see eye-to-eye during the Civil War, one thing was clear: They both did not agree with President Johnson in his coddling of Southern whites who were contesting the Reconstruction bills passed by Congress. When Johnson suspended Stanton as Secretary of War, he asked Grant to take over temporarily, which Grant agreed to if only to avoid having someone appointed by Johnson that sympathized with the president.

Now wearing two hats as war secretary and general of the U.S., Army Grant proceeded to antagonize Johnson's supporters in the Cabinet with his pre-Reconstruction stand. His enemies tried to dismiss him as a naïve military man, but, in reality, Grant was growing his political legs as he continued to gather support for his views on how the problem in the South should be addressed. He was a fervent advocate of the post-war goals of Abraham Lincoln, which were to stamp out discrimination against blacks, and keep the Southern whites in line to prevent another rebellion from brewing.

As calls for Johnson's impeachment started brewing, the embattled president tried to get Grant on his side, querying him on whose side he would stand should orders arrive to arrest the president. Grant proved rather apolitical saying simply that he would "follow orders." Grant's even-handed stance on sensitive matters and his adherence to law and the limitations of his office drove the media and public into a frenzy to recruit him and run for president. When prodded for his views on the matter, Grant simply replied that taking on the presidency would mean taking a pay cut, indicating that matters of personal economic security was most paramount in his mind.

Things came to a head, however, in November 1867, when the House Judiciary Committee voted to start articles of impeachment against Johnson primarily for his violation of the Tenure in Office Act as well as some relatively trivial charges. The calls for Grant to consider running for president during the country's fragile moments grew even louder and more strident as most felt that he was the only steady hand that could guide the country through this current turmoil. Johnson however did not give up on Grant and engineered moves to try to show that Grant was on his side. This was meant not only to let some of Grant's veneer to rub off on Johnson, but also to swat away a potential challenger to his presidency.

Things came to a quick and hasty conclusion when the Senate voted in January 1868 to reinstate Stanton as the Secretary of War. Johnson was eager to keep Grant on his side, and pleaded with Grant to refuse stepping down in favor of the returning Stanton. Grant finally put his foot down and given no choice, had to reveal on which side he was on. He rebuffed Johnson and paved the way for Stanton's return.

Angered by Grant's rejection, Johnson embarked on a smear campaign to denigrate Grant and resorted to bringing up his previous alcohol problems. When this did not work, he tried to get William Tecumseh Sherman on his side, a move which also backfired. The world began to close in quickly for Johnson. In early February, Grant was nominated by Republicans in their convention and a few weeks later, the Congress voted 126-47 to impeach Johnson. On March 5, 1868 the impeachment trial for Johnson began with Grant an unseemly presence in the proceedings.

Things quickly turned around for Johnson as he beat impeachment by a single vote. He never forgave Grant for turning against him, but it did not matter. His questionable and often reprehensible actions drove Ulysses S. Grant towards the next part of his amazing life.

TWENTY-EIGHT: Trading Places

His impeachment acquittal did not temper Andrew Johnson's resistance to the Reconstruction Acts one bit. He continued to pursue policies that contradicted the Lincoln principles of post-war reconciliation. Grant, seeing all this unfold, continued to be blasé about his candidacy for President of the United States; still not welcoming it, but also not dismissing it outright. He felt, however, that if he indeed was nominated, he would not turn it down.

On May 21, 1868, in Crosby's Opera House in Chicago, Grant won the Republican nomination on the first ballot in front of 8,000 enthusiastic supporters. As his running mate, the Republicans chose another unassuming personality, House Speaker Schuyler Colfax of Indiana. In Grant, the Republicans had an ally who was committed to black equality including the right to engage in public politics – an ideological extension of the Reconstruction ideals of the party of Lincoln.

On the opposition side, Andrew Johnson sought the nomination of the Democratic Party, which instead selected Horatio Seymour of New York and later on nominated

Francis Preston Blair Jr. of Missouri for his running mate. The Democrats hoped to win a huge number of Southern white votes and a share of disgruntled Northerners who felt the advancement of the Negro cause was proceeding at too hasty a pace.

For his campaign, Grant selected his old pals Rawlins and Charles A. Dana to generate campaign biographies. He brought some generals with him for campaign stops in Leavenworth, Kansas, before returning to Galena in Ohio on August 18 with Comstock and Badeau. Most observers thought that Grant would sail to victory easily in November, and the Democrats attempted to smear him by once again bringing up his alcohol issues. They branded Grant as a traitor and maintained that the United States was a "white man's country."

With the help of his surrogates, Grant courted the plutocrats of the day to help expand his campaign coffers and enlist the help of business not only for his run for his expected presidency. He also made peace with Jewish Americans, making sure that they forgave him for his "ban" on Jews while he was the General of the Army during the Civil War. To consolidate his voting base, he made sure the black people did not forget about his efforts, not only to emancipate them, but to fold them into the fabric of the military and American society.

To his regret, the one person who he could not convince to support his presidency was Sherman, who was sure that politics would corrupt and taint the man that he so respected and loved. Worse, Sherman opposed Reconstruction the way it was crafted by Republicans and the military occupation of the South.

Even without Sherman's support, Grant won the presidency in 1868 with an electoral landslide, 214 – 80, which belied the much closer popular vote, which he won by only 300,000 votes of the 5.7 million cast.

True to form, the President-Elect shunned publicity even as he had to return to Washington D.C. to assume his newest government position. He took a public coach to his house from the train station and slipped back into the city unobtrusively. He immediately began to contemplate who would make up his Cabinet and did so in secret without consulting anyone, which was his first rookie mistake. He was functioning as a military general who did not engage in any consultative process for filling powerful political roles, a very sensitive process filled with political landmines.

His initial appointments included the elevation of his friends to important posts. He made Rawlins Secretary of War and promoted Sherman to General of the Army. He awarded the Secretary of State post to Elihu Washburne before awarding him the diplomatic post in France. The transfer of power from the Johnson administration was acrimonious, and both men traded public barbs with Johnson's being much more venomous, calling Grant a "deceiver" and "debaser," while vowing not to attend Grant's inauguration.

Grant's inauguration speech, true to form, was a passion-starved 1,200 words, and was as unassuming as the man who was taking the mantle of what would soon be called the most powerful position in the world. His victory also helped the 15th Amendment to the Constitution sail into passage. The amendment would formally give a citizen the right to vote no matter what race he belonged to, and passed without trouble, very much unlike what his first year of office would be.

TWENTY-NINE: Spoils of War

Grant immediately made a mistake by choosing a Treasury Secretary who was a businessman, which was expressly forbidden by law. He immediately rectified it and compensated by choosing Hamilton Fish as his Secretary of State. Fish would turn out to somewhat of a stabilizing force for the tenure of his presidency. His other Cabinet appointments, while not controversial in terms of the highly qualified individuals he selected, were criticized because of the lack of process or ideological cohesion.

He found it hard to shed his military mindset in staffing decisions. He tended to hire quickly without consultation or process, but most glaringly, he also fired faster than past presidents. He had controversial hires related to relatives, while his father and father-in-law clashed about their roles in Grant's presidency until their rift became unresolvable.

The term "to the victor belong the spoils" was the order of the day in American politics. Patronage was the accepted practice as his predecessor Abraham Lincoln found out when influence peddlers and job-seekers cluttered the White House corridors and stairs when he was president. Lincoln and

186

Grant tried their best to resist falling under the spell of the patronage system and mostly succeeded, but friends and relatives still found their way into various positions in their administrations.

Despite the patronage system, a very little-known achievement of Grant's administration was the hiring of a record number of blacks and Jews in official positions. Grant, it turns out, did not play only lip service to racial equality but actually practiced it when he got into a position of power. He extended his sensitivity to racial injustice to foreign affairs by acting on racial persecution in Turkey and Romania.

Another landmark of Grant's administration was the colossal expansion of the federal government as several new federal departments were created. By the end of his first term, the federal government was the biggest employer in the country. The increasing centralization had the effect of a new sense of nationhood by welding the states closer.

Ironically the war, which cost hundreds of thousands of lives, also resulted in a booming economy as war contracts fueled a burgeoning economy, especially in the North. New technologies in telegraph and railroad created a new continental economy, creating new industries and a massive variety of consumer goods. This eclipsed by far the agricultural–based economy of the South, which depended on slaves.

The burgeoning economy ushered in the "Gilded Age", in which colossal new fortunes were made. Unfortunately, the amount of money also created unprecedented temptation for corruption and illicit profits. Businesses began to lobby for land grants, government contracts, tax breaks, and other favors that forced the dominant Republican Party to balance its idealistic abolitionist past and the new business dominant future.

Aside from shepherding the country into a new age, Grant also oversaw the transformation of Washington from a small straggling village into a modern metropolis possessing water and gas mains, sewage systems, and paved roads. Together with Julia they also transformed the White House into a showcase worthy of opulent parties that became much-awaited social events.

The lofty office of the President of the United States did not change the inner Grant significantly. He maintained the quiet unobtrusive façade that endeared him to those that knew him best. He also reaffirmed that his utmost priority, even above duty to the country, was his commitment to family. He secured the use of a beach

house in Long Branch in New Jersey, where he could enjoy private and quiet times with Julia and his children, the most enjoyable part of his life before and during his presidency.

THIRTY: We Are All Americans

Grant continued to make the abolitionist goals of ensuring the welfare of the freed black slaves. He continued to make the federal government the tool by which he could achieve his vision. He led the creation of institutions like the Bureau of Education to help further the welfare of black people. But he did not confine himself to black people when he pursued the goals of American equality and fairness.

He saw the plight of the American Indian as one that required his immediate attention. He planned to extend citizenship through a gradual process recognizing their rights as true Americans. Given their nomadic lifestyle and the desire of many to hunt them to extinction, he proposed to gather Indians and place them in the safety of reservations, a system that while fraught with many inconsistencies and inadequacies is a system still in place today.

The other side of this compassionate heart was the tenacity and obsessiveness of his personality developed through his military training leadership. While these traits were assets during wartime, it often became a liability to Grant during peacetime.

This dogged stubbornness was most apparent on his desire to annex the tiny half-island on Hispaniola (today's Dominican Republic) called Santo Domingo. His still underdeveloped political radar made him prey to silvery tongued opportunists who tried to curry his patronage. Given glowing reports by speculators about the supposed wondrous features of Santo Domingo, Grant wanted to leverage America's expansionist goals that saw the annexation of Alaska among others. More than just new territory, he saw Santo Domingo as a destination where disenfranchised blacks could settle and start a new life.

In true military fashion he put together plans for annexation and presented it to a startled Cabinet that wondered why they weren't consulted first before the ambitious plans were drawn up. This was another big mistake - without drumming the requisite public and political support, he tried to engineer a major initiative that would require significant national resources, not to mention that he was risking potential conflict with Spain, which also was laying claims to Santo Domingo. When the citizens of Spain found out the planned annexation by the United States, there was a large outcry of protest and defiance.

In the midst of the gravity of the Santo Domingo issue, his close friend and confidante John Rawlins' health continued to deteriorate. He died on September 6, 1869, calling desperately for Grant on his deathbed; the president not being able to be by his side due to transportation conflicts and delays.

THIRTY-ONE: Sin against Humanity

In another display of Grant's tendency to be swayed by shady characters, Grant allowed his name to be included in a scheme to manipulate gold market prices. Early in 1869, two wealthy moguls, Jay Gould and James Fisk Jr., tried to talk Grant's Treasury Department from selling gold with the pretext that increasing the price of gold would drive down the value of the dollar, making exports cheaper and helping local industries by driving up their foreign sales. In reality Gould and Fisk were personally buying up large quantities of gold in the private market betting that with the U.S. Treasury restricting sales, the value of their gold investments would increase significantly.

Grant allowed Gould and Fisk to use his name and that of his brother-in-law Alan Corbin to help corner the gold market and try to drive prices up. When Grant found out about the situation, he disavowed any role in the gold price manipulation and allowed the Treasury Department to sell gold to help reverse the skyrocketing gold prices. The effect of the action was to drive the price of gold from $160 to $133, creating a trading panic that led to Black Friday that resulted in a twenty percent decline in stock prices and the closure of many trading companies.

Mistakes like the gold fiasco saw the rise of many influential critics. One of these was the influential journalist Henry Adams, who criticized Grant's naivete. He joked that the "U.S." in U.S. Grant stood for "Uniquely Stupid." While Adams could only snipe with just a pen, Grant had weightier opponents. One of these would be Massachusetts Senator Charles Sumner, an ardent abolitionist who initially appeared to be Grant's philosophical and political ally.

Their differences began when Sumner wanted England to fully accept responsibility for the damages that the *CSS Alabama* inflicted on the Union during the Civil War. Sumner went as far as demanding a $2 billion-dollar payment from England to compensate the United States for the damages. Grant and his Secretary of State Hamilton Fish, eager to put the issue behind them, would have settled for England expressing their regret that a ship of British manufacture was used against the Union during the war.

Outside of the *CSS Alabama* rift with Sumner, Grant continued to place a premium on his program of improving the welfare of the black people. Under his watch the Fifteenth Amendment to the constitution was passed on February 3 1870 giving black people the right to vote.

But while the amendment seemed to be a victory for abolitionists and just plain common sense and fairness, it was met with a vigorous backlash from the South, which still was not square with the notion that black people could ever be equal with whites. Apart from this, he continued to make significant imprints on the nation when the Supreme Court increased its number of justices from eight to nine, and when he nominated his first two justices for the high court.

THIRTY-TWO: The Darkest Blot

In his second year in office, Grant's rift with Charles Sumner continued to manifest itself in public disagreements about foreign policy, where Sumner wanted to be the voice of foreign policy of the country. Grant swallowed his pride and walked to Sumner's house on January 2, 1870, to personally appeal to the senator to help him pass the Bill for Santo Domingo's annexation. On March 15, 1870, however, Sumner's Senate Foreign Relations Committee voted to defeat Grant's annexation bill. On March 24, Sumner himself launched a four-hour tirade on the Senate floor against the bill.

Grant uncharacteristically lashed out against his Cabinet for not helping him sustain the treaty. He urged Fish to help him lobby the Senate to urge the treaty along, but on June 30 Grant failed to get the required two-thirds vote to pass the treaty.

Enraged at his loss, Grant vented his anger on John Motley, who Grant appointed as ambassador to England. Using Motley's supposed opposition to Grant's position on the CSS Alabama, Grant dismissed Motely from his ambassador position on July 1, the day after the Santo Domingo treaty was defeated in the Senate. Understandably, Sumner was apoplectic about Motley's dismissal and raged against Grant's dismissal of a man that Sumner sponsored for the diplomatic position. Sumner's feud with Grant continued to simmer and was about to boil over.

In the meantime, Grant had to address the nagging problems in the south as blacks continued to suffer under white supremacists, especially the Ku Klux Klan. To battle the problem, he dispatched his new Attorney-General, Amos T. Akerman, to the South. Akerman immediately began to consolidate law enforcement resources to coordinate the war against the white supremacists. He created the Department of Justice and appointed the country's first solicitor general, Benjamin Bristow to coordinate cases with federal marshals and U.S. attorneys.

In the mid-term elections in November, 1870, the Republican's majority in Congress shrank by 32 seats and in the Senate, 4; but they still maintained their majorities. The election results were an indication that many white people, even in the North, resented the ceaseless advancement of blacks who were beginning to win elections for public posts.

Despite the losses in Congress, Grant and Akerman

197

continued their prosecution of crimes perpetrated against black people. Even as many whites dismissed the violence as fairy tales dreamed up the Grant administration, the government crusade continued. Grant issued an order to deploy federal troops against white supremacists. His Justice Department helped prosecute the crimes and the newly created Secret Service pitched in with detective work. Under Akerman's direction, hundreds of arrests and convictions were made. By 1872 the Ku Klux Klan was effectively wiped out.

In a huge loss to the Grant administration, Akerman quit his position burdened by the massive workload brought on by his quixotic campaign against giant commercial enterprises, especially the railroads.

THIRTY-THREE: A Dance of Blood

As 1870 was coming to a close, Grant began to resuscitate his Santo Domingo obsession and tried to find ways to affect the annexation after he gave reassurances to Santo Domingo president Domingo Baez that he would continue to pursue the issue with American lawmakers. Even in doing so, he knew that he still had one big obstacle in meeting his promise: Charles Sumner.

To circumvent Sumner, Grant tried to have Congress pass a joint resolution that would empower a three-man commission to evaluate the annexation of Santo Domingo. Under this setup, all Grant needed was a simple majority in the Senate to pass the resolution instead of a two-thirds vote. When he heard about Grant's blatant attempt to circumvent his Judiciary Committee, Sumner went on a vitriolic rant, one of the most venomous speeches in U.S. Senate history. His objections notwithstanding Grant selected three people with impeccable credentials to man the panel.

By the time the three men began their deliberations, many observers believed that Grant hoped that the panel would find Santo Domingo to be not worthy of annexation and allow Grant a graceful exit in what was becoming an embarrassing episode. To his dismay, however, the panel wrote a glowing report on Santo Domingo, which meant that the annexation agony would continue to drag on.

Meanwhile, Grant was showing that he was getting properly schooled in political intrigue. He worked for the ouster of Sumner as the head of the Judiciary Committee, which voted 33-9 to have the blustery senator removed. While it was a victory for Grant, many Republicans worried that it could fracture party unity and cost them control over the House or the presidency, maybe even both.

On April 5, 1871, finally free of Sumner's interference, Grant submitted a glowing commissioners' report recommending the annexation of Santo Domingo. By this time, however, any support for annexation had cooled, and the public had no appetite for any annexation of any piece of foreign real estate. Grant's object of obsession dissipated into oblivion, teaching him a lesson about being easily swayed to promote something of questionable value.

In early 1872, Grant returned his attention to the *CSS Alabama* issue as his Secretary of State Hamilton Fish returned to the bargaining table with the British. Grant went against Sumner's wish to punish the British and accepted

England's admission that they should have done more "due diligence" in allowing their ships to be armed for combat against another country. Aside from averting getting into a war with England, the agreement entered the annals of superb diplomacy and ushered in a new spirit of cooperation between both countries. It also immortalized Hamilton Fish as one of the most innovative and competent Secretary of State in U.S. history.

Worn out from the Santo Domingo and *CSS Alabama* battles, Fish submitted his resignation to Grant, who promptly refused it. He still had work to do after all, on the money claims submitted to an international tribunal in Geneva for the damages caused by the British-built ship. This time, Grant did not play it alone advising the Senate and the House Foreign Relations Committee of the developments of the case.

Eventually the Geneva tribunal voted for $15.5 million payment, which was more than acceptable to both countries. Once again, it was considered a diplomatic victory for everyone concerned and the British happily became the bankers of an American economy that was on its way to becoming the most dominant in the world.

THIRTY-FOUR: Vindication

Ulysses S. Grant in his first year of office was an amalgam of contradictory dimensions. He was at the same time an honest and truthful person, but in the Gilded Age surrounded by corrupt and greedy people, some of whom were able to trade on his time for personal and political gain. While he was a sometimes a master of human wisdom, he was also full of naivete which many people including friends and relatives exploited.

In the Gilded Age, it appears that the issue of patronage was a given, the many factors that the country faced for the first time in history: the unbridled growth of heavy industry; the helter-skelter settlement of the West; the protracted rule of the Republican Party; the buccaneering tactics of big business; the enormous wartime expansion of government; and, of course, the rise of ruthless political machines. Grant, in his later years, lamented that he tried to fight fraud and corruption as hard as he could, but the moving parts of the patronage machine were just too complex and overwhelming.

In his first term, Grant attempted to put a damper on patronage politics by creating a civil service function to try to ensure that government positions were staffed by qualified people regardless of their connections. The Civil Service Commission was created to implement this ambitious vision, but its aims fell apart in the face of lukewarm public sentiment and strong pressure from politicians who did not as yet wish to dispense with the patronage system.

In the wake of the failure for the Civil Service Commission to blunt corruption, Grant was resigned to patronage being a necessary condition for a representative government. To him it was an integral part of the democratic system. This outlook was discouraging to "reformers" who saw Grant as representative of the corrupt system, especially when he seemed to insert himself inside complex political maneuvering.

But there was also a double standard that seemed to attach to Grant. Lincoln appeared to get a pass when he was called a master politician, when he employed patronage for political ends, while Grant was criticized as a corrupt opportunist when he did the same thing.

Typical of this is when he got involved with the likes of Senator Roscoe Conkling, who supported Grant in his presidential initiatives and was bestowed control of the lucrative New York Custom House. This was a storehouse of patronage and funds that could be illegally siphoned. It was a massive money generating engine with 1,500 employees and thousands of transactions that passed through its system daily. Many officials jockeyed for control over this golden goose, but Conkling and his minions eventually won out because of his connections with Grant.

Another victim of the patronage system was the American Indian. Even as he was able to install long-time friend and supporter Ely Parker as head of Indian Affairs, Parker fell victim to nefarious interests who saw that a lot of money that could be made in exploiting a porous system and a naïve Indian population that was generally guileless in the wake of looters and thieves. The American Indian was also the victim of an unstoppable and rampaging industrialization that trampled over their lands and lifestyle. Railroad executives pocketed fortunes while they used political connections to bypass laws designed to protect the natives.

This "Grantism" was the rallying cry of reformists that sought to topple Grant and prevent him from winning a second presidential term. Liberal Republicans who were still all in for the taming of the South for the benefit of ex-slaves voiced their disgust at the patronage system which was representative of Grant's governance. They broke off from the mainstream Republican Party and nominated *New York Tribune* editor Horace Greeley as their presidential standard-bearer. In early July 1872 the Democrats closed ranks with the Liberal Republicans and threw their support behind Greeley.

Grant's platform diffused the patronage issue by saying that the Democrats would dismantle the gains made by the Thirteenth through Fifteenth Amendments. Grant got the overwhelming support of blacks and a new voting bloc: feminists. Armed with sharpened political insight, he also won the support of the plutocrats who generously funded his campaign. Helping Grant along was that Greeley was simply a lackluster opponent.

In the general election Grant won by a huge electoral and popular vote margin. Surprisingly, he evoked spiritual themes in his valedictory saying God was preparing the world in His good time for a unified language as one nation free of conflict and war.

THIRTY-FIVE: A Butchery of Citizens

In his second term, Grant immediately had to deal with the
Southern racism that he had battled against most of his adult
life. This time, the setting was Louisiana, where the agitation
against black gains permeated the political process in a violent
way. The race for governor featured Grant-backed
Republican Pitt Kellogg and the Democrat John McEnery.
When black voters publicly backed Kellogg, a racial powder
keg exploded when Kellogg won. Many blacks were
slaughtered and white supremacists did not even allow their
corpses to be retrieved as they decomposed.

Things came to a head when news leaked out that Kellogg
had been "overthrown." The violence continued to escalate
as murders and muggings continued. Grant was alarmed and
felt that a second Civil War was imminent when it came to a
point that elected government officials were being toppled.
He was halfway out of the White House with luggage all
ready, with plans to go to Louisiana to personally rush to its
defense. Instead, he acceded to his advisers and sent old
reliable Philip Sheridan to settle things down. When it was all
over, Sheridan discovered that two thousand blacks had been
murdered since the Civil War ended and that most of the

murders had gone unprosecuted.

The Louisiana issue having been rebuffed, Grant entered a battleground that he had no prior experience in – choosing a Supreme Court Justice. He had problems choosing candidates because of his aversion to consultation with others. He ended up placing four people on the Court: William Strong, Joseph Bradley, Ward Hunt, and Morrison Waite, who Grant nominated to be the Chief Justice.

Grant's second term was notable for family incidents and milestones that had profound effects on him. His father and father-in-law, with whom he had complicated and often testy relationships, died within six months of each other in 1873. He took the death of his father hard while having to stroke the psyche of wife Julia who was inconsolable with her father's passing away. He had Philip Sheridan take his son, Fred, in this company as Lieutenant Colonel, also in 1873, despite criticism by many of favoritism and patronage, a common refrain for Grant.

Ulysses S. (Buck) Grant Jr. graduated from Harvard and entered Columbia Law School during Grant's second term, which was proud moments for the president. Youngest son Jesse entered Cornell during Grant's second term and eventually became a businessman before a short, failed political career.

But it was the apple of Grant's eye Nellie, his only daughter, who provided the most of the family drama in his presidency. She was married in the White House in 1874 when she was just eighteen years old to Algernon Charles Frederick Sartoris, an Englishmen who was connected to the Royal Family of England. The wedding broke her parents' hearts especially, Ulysses Sr.'s, who reportedly broke down and cried minutes after the wedding ceremony. She caused further disappointment when she left for Britain to be with her husband. Tragically she was divorced barely two years later on stories of Sartoris' womanizing. The stormy marriage was of much concern to Grant, who labored to keep news about it from spreading. It was something he would never talk about again in public.

THIRTY-SIX: The Bravest Battle

In the fall of 1873, despite very recent rosy assessments of the economy, many Wall Street firms began to fold, sparking a financial district panic. The "boom" that everyone thought that had recently unfolded was actually based on generous credit and speculation that centered mostly around the over-extended debt of the nation's railways. On September 20, 1873, Wall Street suspended training for ten days as the country looked towards President Grant for some direction.

The severe economic downturn would be termed the "Great Depression," a state of affairs that would be only be eclipsed by the 1930 downturn. The country seemed to lay in economic ruin as unemployment hit record highs, wholesale prices fell by over thirty percent and many factories were left abandoned.

There were various stop gap measures put in place mostly to temporarily sooth frayed nerves. The big solution, however, seemed to be a choice between an inflationary, stimulative increase in money supply or a restrictive policy that would dry up speculative excess and drive down wages and prices. The restrictive policy would also allow the country to establish a gold standard, linking the dollar to metal specie.

On April 14, 1874, legislation was sent to Grant which called for the expansion of the money supply to $400 million, an "inflation bill", which most in Congress felt was the solution to the crisis. After days and sleepless nights of agonizing over whether to sign the bill, he decided to veto it a week later eliciting howls of protest from the expansionists and high praise from those who wanted to return the dollar back to the gold standard including foreign investors.

As the economy continued to be stagnant in the fall of 1874, the Republicans lost control of Congress in a Democrat election tidal wave. The election did not immediately change the fundamentals of the economy. Instead, the biggest effect of the elections was on Reconstruction. Northerners were tired of the attention paid to the rehabilitation of Southern blacks while Southern whites used the Democratic wave to go fast and loose on previously enacted laws on violence on blacks, citizenship, and voting rights.

In Mississippi, for example, a breakaway white man's group agitated against the inordinately high number of blacks in the state assembly. To rectify this, the whites embarked on a combination of violence and voter intimidation to ensure that blacks stayed away from polling places, leading to a large number of blacks losing their elective positions.

A similar situation ensued in Louisiana, where black students and their sympathizers were roughed up as new school integration laws were being implemented. After an appeal to Grant by Louisiana governor Pitt Kellogg, Phil Sheridan was sent to Louisiana for a fact-finding mission. When General Philippa de Trobriand forcibly ejected five Conservatives from the legislature with bayonet-wielding troops, Sheridan, instead of merely being an "observer", announced that he would be suspending the writ of habeas corpus in supporting Kellogg's storm-trooper tactics.

The furor over Sheridan's and Kellogg's tactics was expected. Journalists and other politicians condemned the actions as an overstepping of the bounds of government action. Grant refused to throw Sheridan to the wolves and defended his actions as necessary, citing the violence being done to blacks.

While it marked the beginning of the end of the various Reconstruction Acts passed the Republicans, Grant passed the first Civil Rights Law in 1875 to protect minority rights, the first of its kind in U.S. history and the precursor to the 1964 federal law.

THIRTY-SEVEN: Let No Guilty Man Escape

On the heels of the civil rights fiascos in the South, Grant's administration found itself again caught up in controversy over patronage politics. This time the issue revolved around the illegal siphoning of taxes on whiskey sales. The characters in the drama were Grant's old friend John McDonald and Grant's aide Horace Babcock. McDonald, who Grant had appointed as internal revenue supervisor in Arkansas and Missouri, siphoned off millions of dollars of tax money which was used to shower patronage funds to politicians to help them win office and obtain political favors. This was accomplished by forging documents and filing false returns to cover up the theft.

Beginning in 1874, Grant's new Treasury Secretary Benjamin Bristow began to investigate the alleged tax scam. In May 1875, Bristow struck hard at the ring and uncovered their massive theft operation proving that McDonald masterminded the operation, while Babcock tipped off the perpetrators before Bristow's agents raided the internal revenue offices. It would start off a nearly one-year drama that showcased how Grant could be blinded by his close ties to people, which more often than not harmed his personal reputation.

After investigations revealed that McDonald had masterminded the fraud, McDonald broke down and admitted to the swindle. Together with internal revenue agent John Joyce, McDonald was sentenced to three years in prison. Bristow's investigation further revealed that Babcock had provided inside information to McDonald based on his internal knowledge of investigations because of his proximity to information in Grant's law enforcement administration.

When indictments were handed down against Babcock for fraud and obstruction of justice, Grant came to Babcock's defense. He called his own Treasury Secretary's investigation a witch hunt, especially when his brother Orvil and brother-in-law Fred Dent were implicated. The acrimony between Grant and Bristow had Bristow considering resignation more than a few times only to be convinced by Hamilton Fish. Grant's passionate defense of Babcock included a lengthy deposition, which was instrumental in Babcock's acquittal. In a cruel twist of fate, Grant found out immediately after Babcock's acquittal that Babcock had frittered away $40,000 of Grant's money because illegal deals had been made with

Jay Gould and James Fisk. Instead of confronting Babcock, he continued to voice his support for him, but had him reassigned to a much lower revenue post, where he drowned soon after at the age of forty-eight. The scandal put a permanent stamp on Grant's proclivity towards blind, implicit trust of men.

His second term sadly marked the end of Reconstruction and the beginning of a new brand of "slavery" in the South. In choosing between political expediency and the protection of black civil and voting rights, Grant chose the latter. It would lead to a permanent disenfranchisement of blacks in Mississippi and other Southern states for many years to come. It was not a lost second term, however. He called for the expansion for public education, especially for black children and for the separation of church and state in public schools, initiatives that are felt to this day.

After two terms in office Grant had enough of the pressures and travails of public office. While he could still run for a third term and was still considered a hero based on his Civil War exploits, Republicans felt that it was time for him to leave the nomination to someone else. Against the wishes of Julia Grant, who fell in love with the pomp and splendor of life in the White House, Grant formally announced that he

214

would not seek the nomination for a third term in office.

THIRTY-EIGHT: Saddest of the Falls

Unfortunately for Grant, the scandals did not end with the Babcock fiasco. His Interior Secretary Columbus Delano resigned in shame after he was alleged to have dispensed profitable Indian trading posts. Benjamin Bristow once again led the investigation of the scandal that also implicated Grant's brother Orvil. In an embarrassing turn of events, Orvil admitted that he had lobbied Grant for the posts which Grant agreed to. Orvil also casually admitted that he skimmed money from his posts but insisted that his brother knew nothing about his wrongdoing.

Finally, there was William W. Belknap, who was Grant's Secretary of War and admitted that he had accepted bribes from businessman Caleb P. Marsh, who had obtained an Indian trading post currently held by a certain John Evans. Evans made quarterly payments to Marsh and Carrie Belknap, the Secretary's wife, who was often criticized for her lavish and extravagant lifestyle, to keep his trading post. After Mrs. Belknap died, Evans' payments were re-directed to Secretary Belknap himself. Grant's role in the scandal was that he accepted Belknap's resignation, which had inside information that he was going to be impeached. A resignation meant that the impeachment articles would be difficult to pursue. As a result, Belknap was not impeached but his and Grant's name would forever be sullied by the incident.

The final scandals related to Grant's administration revealed a lot about the president. Most important is that Grant himself did not profit or had not been personally involved in any scandal - his biggest failure was the way he managed the downfall of the perpetrators. But except in a very few cases, he was insistent about their prosecution - his administration produced the most charges against erring staff members than any previous president. All of the scandals were perpetrated in the last two years of his final term that obscured the huge accomplishments during the first six years of his administration. It was also evident that a lot of the manufactured outrage against him came from legislators who were keen on dismantling Reconstruction.

The scandals out of the way, attention turned to who was going to replace Grant on the presidential ticket, and what kind of agenda was going to be pursued by the Republicans going forward. While it was agreed that Reconstruction needed to be continued, there was less consensus on how its provisions were going to be enforced, especially on the question of the deployment of federal forces in incidents of racial violence and discrimination.

In the end, the Republicans nominated Rutherford Hayes for their candidate. Hayes' platform would run almost counter to Grant's with less focus on Reconstruction and the establishment of a civil service system that was seen as a jab to what he privately maintained was a corrupt Grant administration. The Democratic Party nominated Samuel Tilden from New York, an avowed critic of Reconstruction.

As a lame-duck president on his way out, Grant wanted to leave office on a high note and touted the 100th anniversary of the country's founding, which would be highlighted by a massive celebration in Philadelphia in July 1876. Instead of celebrating, the last few months of his administration would be embroiled in settling the Indian question which had come to a boil as members of the militant Sioux tribe stretched the limits of government tolerance. Highlighted by the now famous massacre of George Custer's troops in Little Big Horn, the war against the Indians would eventually turn out to be what many describe as a genocide. More than any president, however, he tried to address the Indian "crisis" in the most humane way possible given the ever-widening gulf between breakneck Westward expansion and ancient Indian traditions.

As a reminder of how the racial question was not going to disappear any time soon, a violent racial incident on July 4, 1876 was ignited in South Carolina on the exact date of the country's centennial presaging what the nation's character would be like after Grant left office. Hundreds of blacks were killed or wounded in rioting, which proceeded with impunity under the helpless watch of state officials. It would seem that the end of Grant's presidency would also mean the end of the black man's progress towards assimilation.

THIRTY-NINE: Redeemers

Grant became but an interested observer in the 1876 elections, but was dismayed to see Reconstruction being dismantled piece by piece. His final days were spent on mulling the dispatching of troops in violent flashpoints in the South, as he went just short of dispatching troops to Mississippi and South Carolina. In the campaign, Democrats understandably ran on taking apart Reconstruction policies and dwelling on the scandals that rocked the Grant administration. The Supreme Court had helped along this cause by issuing opinions that watered down the Fourteenth and Fifteenth Amendments.

On election day, Republicans seemed poised to lose the presidential elections as Democrat candidate Samuel Tilden garnered more votes than Rutherford Hayes. The electoral count, however, ended up with only 184 votes, one short of the required 185 with the 19 electoral votes of Florida, Louisiana, and South Carolina still in doubt. If it turned out that Hayes somehow managed to win the contested 19 remaining electoral votes, he would win the required 185 votes to win the presidency.

This was an unwelcome development for Grant who was counting on a peaceful transition from public to private life. Instead, he would be thrust into a dispute that could end up in a constitutional crisis. Recounts needed to be impartially conducted in the three contested states and there was great concern that with so much riding on the recounts tampering, intimidation, and even violence could ensue. In fact, there were already reports of disturbances in the three states as the recounts loomed.

Because the electors could not cast their final vote on December 6 as the law required, a non-partisan review commission needed to be convened. By the end of January 1877, Grant signed a Congressional bill that created a bipartisan and independent Electoral Commission composed of five Supreme Court justices and five members of each house, fifteen members in all. Grant saw this as a welcome means to pave the way for his graceful exit, and finally "escape" the limelight.

In late February the electoral commission by an 8-7 voted declared that Hayes had won all 19 remaining electoral votes, finally putting an end to Grant's anguish and signaled that at least he could say goodbye to the White House.

In his last days as president, the common assessment was that Grant was bedeviled more by personality issues rather than his policies, which, over time, history would consider as excellent. His tenacity that bordered on obstinacy was a major fault as this prevented him from clearly thinking out major issues. Complicating matters was that he was presiding over a tumultuous time when a country was still very much racially divided and was growing in every way – size, population, technology, and especially the economy. In addition his foreign policy would be graded as excellent not only by Americans but more importantly by foreign observers.

What he and Abraham Lincoln did for slaves during and after the Civil War gives him an honored place in the history of the United States. As with slavery, he got the big issues right, even as he misfired on the smaller ones.

Everyone who met with him as he was about to leave the White House talked about how weary and tired he was. He had after all borne the country's troubles on his shoulders and appeared to have no more energy to carry on. He would ever be grateful to his Secretary of State Hamilton Fish, who somehow managed to stay during Grant's entire presidency and served as the political version of his late friend John Rawlins – helping him navigate through always unpredictable and choppy political waters.

His joyfulness in leaving the White House was matched by
the regret and sadness that Julia had in leaving it. Still, they
faced their opposite sentiments with the same understanding
and love that they had in handling everything else in their
marriage. His devotion to his wife and family was ultimately
secondary to his love for his country. William Tecumseh
Sherman, who had a complicated but respectful relationship
with Grant, said that where George Washington was
identified with the birth of the United States, Grant will
forever be identified with its preservation.

PART FOUR: A LIFE OF REFLECTION

FORTY: The Wanderer

There were two overriding concerns of Ulysses Grant after leaving office: Where he was going to get money to finance his post-presidential life, and where he was going to live. These concerns were temporarily shelved however by his life-long desire to travel to Europe. For his retinue, Grant would bring along Julia and Jesse Grant, a maid, a guide, and a journalist, John Russell Young, who was a testament to Grant's now honed political instincts, no longer willing to separate his public from his private life.

When he left from Philadelphia on May 17, 1877 for England, the thousands who showed up to see him off was a portent of the public reception that he was about to receive in what would turn out to be a twenty-eight-month cruise around the world. On May 28, Grant's contingent landed in Liverpool and were met by a huge cheering throng that showed that their world tour would not be a private and anonymous tourist jaunt. Even before they arrived in London, Ulysses Grant was already being set up by the British press as the country's best friend and the singular biggest American figure in history.

In London, they were once again met by a large adoring throng and were invited by Queen Victorian and her Court for a magnificent reception. While they were looked down somewhat as unpolished rubes, Ulysses and Julia Grant held their own and never capitulated on their rough-hewn Americanism. After meeting famed composer Richard Wagner in Belgium, they returned to England, where Grant gave a rousing speech on labor in Newcastle in front of thousands of British working class including a tearful black Briton who saw Grant as a life-size hero.

On October 24, 1877, they arrived in Paris, where they stayed for five weeks. With a little more anonymity, the Grants were able to sample the sights and delights of the city. In December, the U.S. government allowed them the use of the man-of-war cruiser, the *Vandalia,* which brought them to Italy, Egypt and Israel, where Grant was the first American president to have ever visited the country.

He met legendary statesmen like Otto von Bismarck of Germany and Czar Alexander II in St. Petersburg, Russia. Just as they were finishing their voyage with stops in Austria and Spain, Secretary of the Navy Richard W. Thompson offered Grant to sail to Japan, India, and China on *Richmond,* the government steamer. In Asia they were met by hundreds of thousands of people in China and Hong Kong, crowds never before seen by Grant in any assembly.

They finally left Japan for San Francisco in September 1879 with Grant now faced with nagging questions about his future career, the location of his home, and, most importantly, if he was going to run for a third term. He went home to Galena after an appearance in Chicago and emotional trips to cities that were parts of the old Confederate States. A crowd of 350,000, the biggest crowd that had ever attended a Grant gathering in America, had given him some inspiration to once again become the President of the United States.

FORTY-ONE: Master Spirit

While he was travelling around the world for over two years, the fading promises of Reconstruction were a nagging issue that was constantly on the back of his mind. When he was firmly back on U.S. soil, the thoughts quickly transformed into reality. His old friends Sheridan and Sherman broached the topic of Grant running again for president so that he could recover some of the ground that Reconstruction had lost over the past four years under more centrist Republican administration and a surging Democrat opposition. His old sponsor Elihu Washburne advised Grant that there was a real chance that he could once again win the Republican nomination but that he would have to run against George Washington's theory of limiting a presidency to two terms. There were still many positives, however, for a third Grant campaign; almost all of it revolving around his sterling military success and his affiliation with Abraham Lincoln. Still being unsure about his income prospects and where he would be establishing residence, the prospects of a presidency started looking very attractive.

In the midst of Grant's return and the rumblings about his return to politics, his brother and former co-worker at their father's tanning company, Orvil, surfaced as an itinerant vagrant walking the streets of New York penniless and homeless. In a sad footnote to an eventful family narrative for Ulysses Grant, Orvil died a year later with Grant choosing not to attend the funeral.

Back in Chicago in June 1880, Grant showed up confident that he could secure the nomination from among a field of candidates that did not have the name recognition as he did. No one was after all a former General of the Army and held office for the position that the Republican presidential nominees were all angling for – No one but U.S. Grant. Expected to breeze through the nomination in the first few ballots, Grant lost in the thirty-sixth ballot to James Garfield after leading in almost every ballot leading to the final vote. In the analysis that followed Grant's stunning loss, most ascribed it to the heavy-handed tactics by Grant's campaign team led by party operatives Roscoe Conkling, Simon Cameron, and John Logan, who most agreed had split up the Republican Party.

While Grant expressed some relief for not having to deal with another four years of scrutiny and pressure, he regretted not being in the saddle to continue his fight for principles. Julia Grant was less forgiving and fatalistic about the loss and maintained that her husband was treated shabbily by his own party.

Despite having lost the primary, Grant felt that his vision could still be realized through the presidency of Garfield. Like Grant, Garfield was born in Ohio and served as a general in the Civil War. He campaigned for him energetically and seemed to develop a knack for public speaking that even author Mark Twain, who accompanied Grant in his campaign stops, took notice of.

On election day in 1880, Grant's efforts on behalf of Garfield paid off as Garfield became the fourth straight Republican to win a presidential race since the end of the Civil War. It seemed that Grant would have a new lease on life, and his post-presidential life was now looking up. He was bitter that somehow the presidency had impoverished him and now he was ready to make up for lost time and money.

FORTY-TWO: A Miserable Dirty Reptile

After Garfield's election, Grant expected to be appointed to a high position in the new presidential administration - maybe even a Cabinet appointment. When Garfield began to appoint people that Grant did not approve of, their relationship quickly soured. They had a heated exchange of words which seemed to drive a permanent wedge between them.

The rift continued until July 2 1881, when a mentally imbalanced Charles J. Guiteau, a frustrated politician, shot Garfield in Washington D.C. Guiteau had stalked Grant just a few months earlier and even struck a conversation with him upon which Grant irritably shooed him away. As Garfield's life hung in the balance, Grant was consumed by guilt for his previous acrimonious interaction with the dying president. He reached out to Garfield's wife and kept close tabs on Garfield's condition. Garfield finally passed away on September 19, 1881, leaving Grant disconsolate for not having been able to mend fences with the fallen president, and, according to his son Fred, he wept bitterly as soon as he heard the news.

Grant's political fortunes were ironically revived when Vice-President Chester Arthur took over the presidency. Arthur took Grant's recommendations for various positions to heart and his appointments were welcomed by Grant heartily. He now needed to change his economic fortunes as well.

Grant still needed a steady income for himself and Julia, and he was earnestly looking for ways to generate a sizeable fund from which he could finance his family's lifestyle. A promising railroad project in the West did not pan out as planned and continued Grant's streak of bad luck with business ventures. Luckily for Grant, wealthy admirers from Wall Street created a "Presidential Retiring Fund" of $250,000 from which he could draw interest while another donor group provided him $100,000 that allowed him to purchase his New York residence.

Things seemed to look up when his son Buck entered into a partnership with a young financier named Ferdinand Ward and his partner a balding, stout businessman, James D. Fish. The slick-talking Ward convinced the Grants to put in almost $2 million of their money into Ward's investment fund. Ward seemed so adept in Finance that Ohio senator Allen Thurman saw Ward's potential as a future Treasury Secretary. Grant's sons even formed an investment company with Ward, calling it Grant and Ward. While the Grant name figured prominently in signage, all operations and accounting were done under Ward's direction.

Ferdinand Ward dazzled prospective investors giving examples of clients who were making 20% or more per month. The gullible Grant, thoroughly impressed by the 29-year old Ward, invested everything that he had. When the money first started coming in, an increasingly sickly Grant for once enjoyed a measure of financial freedom thanks to the great Ferdinand Ward's amazing investment model.

Unbeknownst to the Grants and other investors, Ward and Fish were running a Ponzi scheme where the money paid back to investors came from new money that was invested. Whatever "income" a Ponzi fund made, it was dwarfed by the personal withdrawals of Ward and Fish, a mechanism that would soon come to a halt when no new monies would come in. Their fund's debt was a staggering $16 million in the end. In 1884, when the scheme came crashing down, Ward came to Grant one last time and asked him to plead with railroad tycoon William Henry Vanderbilt for $150.000 to bail out their failing enterprise. Once again fooled by the persuasive Ward, Grant mortgaged his house and memorabilia to Vanderbilt, who quickly gave him a check that would never be paid back.

The ever-trusting Grant had made his last fatal error in his business career allowing Ward to take away every penny that he and Julia owned; reducing their money to just a couple of hundred dollars. Perhaps the most devastating aspect of the Ferdinand Ward deceit was that he would not be able to provide financial sustenance to Nellie Grant, whose life in Europe was financed almost entirely by Grant. He and Julia were now destitute - their home would soon be taken away from him and Grant himself having no source of income.

After being initially mocked by critics in the press, the nation coalesced around its hero and he was able to get by with the generosity of friends. It was surely not the existence that a former General of the Army and President of the United States would ever envision for himself, but there was still the matter of providing Julia and himself a living. At sixty-two years old Grant was penniless, homeless, and jobless.

FORTY-THREE: Taps

Their finances shattered, the Grants moved out of their New York home and settled in their Long Branch vacation home having long shed their servants and accoutrements of luxury that they briefly enjoyed. Julia Grant was now reduced to cooking at home, her role reduced to that of an elderly housewife. Totally divested of his money, Grant was also losing his health, as he was now mostly on crutches because of arthritis and other ailments, including a nagging pain in his neck and throat. He consulted with a physician, Jacob Mendez Da Costa, who discovered that Grant had a growth on the roof of his mouth. He would avoid seeing a specialist while he pondered on how to finance his retirement.

When the editors of *The Century* suggested that he write his memoirs to enable him to earn some money, he decided to take the leap into writing. While his first attempts were weak and sophomoric, he eventually became proficient with the help of magazine editors who helped him hone his craft. After some time, he finally saw a leading mouth specialist, Dr. John H. Douglas, who examined him thoroughly and confirmed that he had three cancerous lesions in his mouth. He smoked his last cigar in November 1884, as he was now wracked with excruciating pain in his mouth; and drinking and eating became painful adventures.

Despite the pain, he had found a new passion with writing and was engrossed in his craft for up to five hours a day. He would be huddled in a blanket and wearing a cap while he reclined on a chair, a bearded recluse reduced to a withering shell of his old self. Even lying down now became a painful task and he was advised to lie on his side curled up to relieve the pressure on his neck and mouth. This was an era in which cancer was untreatable, and the relief of pain was the only source of comfort to Grant, who many times was wishing for a quick death.

After moving back to their New York apartment, Grant started negotiations with *Century* regarding the royalties that he was going to earn for his memoirs. He was offered a 10% royalty rate, which had no meaning to Grant, who was tone-deaf to business numbers and deals. When his friend, author Mark Twain, heard about the deal, he offered his own more lucrative set of terms, which Grant accepted, signing a deal in January 1885. Twain was sure that Grant's memoirs was going to be a hit and together with his publisher they already mapped out a marketing plan for the book. He still had his eye on politics as he wrote his memoirs. In the 1884 elections,

Grant was pleased that James Blaine won the Republican nomination, but the joy was quickly extinguished when he was upset by Grover Cleveland, a lawyer from New Jersey in another closely contested presidential race.

In March 1885, Grant's physical situation was laid out in the newspapers for the entire world to see. They reported that he was on his death bed and did not have much longer to live. Washington D.C. was aghast as they immediately reconsidered a bill to reinstate Grant to a "retired general" position, which he had relinquished earlier. After much deliberation in honor of the man who had served his country like no other, Congress awarded him his position in a midnight bill, and the Senate clock was actually moved back two hours to accommodate a vote just as the outgoing president was about to leave office.

Grant immediately immersed himself into writing in a race against the clock against a death that was quickly approaching. After a regrettable falling out with his old friend Adam Badeau, he took on a punishing writing schedule. He eventually lost his voice after a tumor the size of two fists grew around his neck. A close friend, Joseph W. Drexel, gave him the free use of a Saratoga Springs, an upscale resort in Upstate New York to relieve Grant from the harshness of the humid New York summer. He did beat death by a hair finishing "The Personal Memoirs of U. S. Grant," which was widely viewed as a masterpiece after its publication.

He put the finishing touches on a remarkable life by making sure that Julie was provided for and that he made amends with people that he had wronged. He met with the relatives of Confederate generals that he bitterly battled during the war to drive home the notion that they were all the citizens of the same United States. As he was for most of his life he was unobtrusive and quiet in death passing away in his sleep on July 23, 1885 at 8:08 a.m.

As expected, the country went through an extended period of national mourning. His funeral was attended by all living presidents as his caisson was hefted by a contingent that included both former Union and Confederate soldiers. The man who had lived a complicated life that was mostly free of pomp and fanfare in the service of his country was finally properly accorded a rousing goodbye by the people that he had selflessly served.

Conclusion

Many biographies have been written about Ulysses S. Grant, and most have, rightly, elevated him among the deified ranks of great American heroes. Some biographies have even dismissed him as a butcher, wantonly frittering the lives of hundreds of thousands of men for the sake of military glory. While there were twelve generals who went on to become President of the United States, only one, Grant, fought in wars against other countries AND against his own countrymen. The first president to serve two terms since the fiery Andrew Jackson, Grant was the quintessential bigger-than-life American icon who led its armies and then its nation, during what is inarguably the most difficult time in its history since its formation.

In many ways, Ulysses S. Grant is like most Americans, or what most Americans aspire to be. He came from humble beginnings, worked hard and, purposefully with integrity, overcame great odds, obstacles, and criticism; but still came out on top. Then also, he had many failures – he wiped out financially, and occasionally stumbled through his generalship of the U.S. Army and presidency, two of the hardest jobs that an American had to fill in ordinary times, but whose hardships multiplied during the worse of American eras when the mortal enemy of each American was another American. He had his famous bouts with alcoholism, probably his biggest personal foible, and his cantankerous bouts with an imperious father and father-in-law.

It is harder to find what not to like in Grant than finding what is good and admirable about him. The praiseful voices of Walt Whitman and the soldiers, who both fought for and against him, are resoundingly much louder than the few who found and continue to find cracks in the general's armor.

But more than Grant, Chernow brings to vivid life the seemingly endless number of characters that dotted not only Grant's amazing life, but that of the United States; at a time when its very existence was on life support as it opened a gaping self-inflicted wound heralding the entrée of characters like Grant, Abraham Lincoln, and Robert Lee in its operating theater.

All three men survived the horrendous four years of the Civil War, but it was only Grant who lived its horrors for the duration, and then came back to lead the country in what could be considered as the most turbulent time of peace in a country just growing out of its painful adolescence.

Final Thoughts

Hey! Did you enjoy this book? We sincerely hope you thoroughly enjoyed this short read and have gotten immensely valuable insights that will help you in any areas of your life.

Would it be too greedy if we ask for a review from you?

It takes 1 minute to leave 1 review to possibly influence 1 more person's decision to read just 1 book which may change their 1 life. Your 1 minute matters and we value it and thank you so much for giving us your 1 minute. If it sucks, just say it sucks. Period.

FREE BONUS

<u>P.S. Is it okay if we overdeliver?</u>

Here at Abbey Beathan Publishing, we believe in overdelivering way beyond our reader's expectations. Is it okay if we overdeliver?

Here's the deal, we're going to give you an extremely valuable cheatsheet of "Accelerated Learning". We've partnered up with Ikigai Publishing to present to you the exclusive bonus of "Accelerated Learning Cheatsheet"

What's the catch? We need to trust you… You see, we want to overdeliver and in order for us to do that, we've to trust our reader to keep this bonus a secret to themselves. Why? Because we don't want people to be getting our exclusive accelerated learning cheatsheet without even buying our books itself. Unethical, right?

Ok. Are you ready?

Simply Visit this link: http://bit.ly/acceleratedcheatsheet

We hope you'll enjoy our free bonuses as much as we've enjoyed preparing it for you!

Free Bonus #2: Free Book Preview of Summary: God: A Human History

The Book at a Glance

God: A Human History is a journey through the history of mankind's attempt to know God from ancient times to the advent of Islam. Just like in Genesis, the book begins at the beginning of time but it presents the story from a scientific perspective. It then follows Adam and Eve's progress as hunter-gatherers to farmers and finally to civilization builders, describing the changes that occurred within their minds and in their societies as their belief in God evolved. At the very end, it reveals a startling secret that is a product of Reza Asians' religious scholarship and personal search for the truth of what God is.

Part One: The Embodied Soul

Chapter 1: Adam and Eve in Eden

The first chapter applies the creation story to what science has found so far and describes what could be the very root of the invention of religion – the soul.

Chapter 2: The Lord of the Beasts

The Lord of the Beasts narrates how prehistoric people viewed divinity as someone who is similar to themselves but with power over nature.

Chapter 3: The Face in the Tree

The Face in the Tree further explains the ancient notion of the embodiment of the soul by describing the instinctive compulsion to see humanity in nature.

Part Two: The Humanized God

Chapter 4: Spears into Plows

Having discovered agriculture, humans experienced changes in their worldview and the gods changed along with it.

Chapter 5: Lofty Persons

The idea of gods as lofty persons became more prominent and this idea spread through different lands, producing various gods.

Chapter 6: The High God

There have been times in history when some people claimed a god was the only god there was; this chapter tells the story of humanity's first attempts at monotheism.

Part Three: What is God?

Chapter 7: God is One

Moses came to know a God who proclaimed that He is the only

243

one there is, and this time, the goal to worship a singular god became successful

Chapter 8: God is Three

Jesus' arrival as described in the New Testament implied a predicament to the notion that God is a singular god, thus, Church leaders sought a way to explain that God is three in one.

Chapter 9: God is All

From the deserts of Arabia comes Islam, and unlike Christianity, its god is one without a human image.

Introduction: In Our Image

As a child, Reza Aslan imagined that God was like his father, but larger, and had magical powers. He saw him sitting in a throne among the clouds – his voice boomed when he was angry, but he could also laugh and cry. He wasn't sure where he got this description, whether he had glimpsed it in a painting, learned in a storybook, or he was simply born with the notion. Despite this, he acknowledged that according to research, people usually think about God as a human with supernatural abilities.

He grew up fascinated by spirituality and religion, wanting to know what God is really like. He wanted to feel the presence of God in his life, but he perceived a great gap between him and the deity. When he was a teen, he left Islam and became Christian like his friends. His new religion gave him hope that he could finally bridge the chasm simply by imagining God as an absolutely perfect human being.

Eventually, this limited conception of God disappointed him and he gave up Christianity and came back to Islam. He had found a new attraction to this religion because it teaches that God cannot be defined by images whether they are human-like or not. On the other hand, he noticed that Muslims cannot help but think of their God in human terms, and they ascribe human vices and virtues,

245

flaws and feelings to it just like others.

He discovered that humanizing the divine is hardwired in the brain, thus it is common in almost all religions. This tendency to bestow human virtues, vices, and even bodies to God stemmed from the need to comprehend the divine, and it reflects in all religions.

Aslan is not claiming that a God doesn't exist and that it's just an invention of humans. For him, there is no proof of both the existence and absence of God. He says that faith, or deciding to believe in something that's beyond the natural world exists, is a choice.

Religion is a language of metaphors and symbols that provides a way for believers to communicate the inexpressible. Throughout religions' history, in almost all of the religions of the world, the greatest metaphor for God is none other than the human being. We bestow on God not only the good qualities such as our ability to show compassion and seek justice, but also the vile things like our greed, aggression, bigotry, bias, and violence.

The consequence of humanizing the divine is to divinize human attributes. God's desires are ours, but without our human limitations, and we convince ourselves that these wishes belong to God. God's actions are based on what we do, but without negative consequences.

This explains why throughout history, religion has led to good and evil deeds, and why two individuals can read the same scriptures

246

and yet still have opposing interpretations.

Aslan realizes that the notion of God he was seeking for was too broad to be confined by any single religious tradition, and experiencing divinity requires dehumanizing God in his consciousness.

Thus, the book is not just a history of how humans have humanized God, it is also a plea to stop ascribing human compulsions to the divine, and instead develop a pantheistic view towards God. This may be done by remembering that we humans have fashioned our God in our image.

CPSIA information can be obtained
at www.ICGtesting.com
Printed in the USA
BVHW041426030919
557429BV00010B/321/P